The
REVOLUTION
in
School
Mathematics

A Challenge for
Administrators
and Teachers

A Report of Regional Orientation Conferences in Mathematics

NATIONAL COUNCIL OF TEACHERS OF MATHEMATICS
1201 SIXTEENTH STREET, N. W., WASHINGTON 6, D. C.

Preface

During the fall of 1960 the National Council of Teachers of Mathematics, with the financial support of the National Science Foundation, conducted eight Regional Orientation Conferences in Mathematics in various parts of the United States. The purpose of these conferences was to give school administrators and mathematics supervisors information that would enable them to provide leadership in establishing new and improved mathematics programs. The distribution of this pamphlet, which contains an edited and up-to-date version of the conference proceedings, is an effort to make this information available to a much wider audience—indeed, to all persons who are interested in the improvement of school mathematics programs.

As a result of the work of many groups (among others, the Commission on Mathematics of the College Entrance Examination Board, the Secondary School Curriculum Committee of the National Council of Teachers of Mathematics, the University of Illinois Committee on School Mathematics, and the School Mathematics Study Group), we are now in a position to make a concerted effort toward rapid improvement of school mathematics. The general pattern is clear, and the necessary materials of instruction are at hand. While these activities have been widely publicized among mathematics teachers, it was felt that administrators and supervisors were not being adequately informed, and that this lack could jeopardize the success of otherwise strong, well-conceived, and well-financed drives to improve school mathematics. The conferences and this pamphlet represent attempts by the Council to solve the problem.

We should like to make it clear that the National Council of Teachers of Mathematics did not participate in the construction of any of the new programs discussed in these pages. The production of textbooks is not a function of the Council. It *is* a function of the Council to focus attention on these new programs without acting as a sponsor for any one of them. This we tried to do in the conferences. We regard each of the new programs as a sample of an improved curriculum in mathematics which deserves the consideration of those interested in devising better mathematics programs.

We hope you will not be distressed by the fact that several programs are offered for your consideration, and that you will not look to the Council for a decision as to which program is best for your school. This pamphlet does not deal with specific questions of this kind, nor does it contain a comparative analysis of the new programs in school mathematics. It is designed to answer more general questions: *What caused the current revolution in school mathematics? What has been done to implement this revolution? What administrative decisions are involved for local school systems?* We hope this pamphlet will be useful to school administrators who must make such decisions. We hope, too, that it will be useful to mathematics teachers, that it will help them interpret the purposes of the new mathematics to colleagues who are not mathematically trained, and that it

iii

will help them to participate more effectively in the formulation of administrative decisions related to the establishment of improved programs in their schools. Moreover, we think our teacher colleagues should know what we have been saying to their superintendents, principals, and supervisors.

We are convinced that the choice of program must be a matter for local decision. The only alternative is a national mathematics program followed by everyone, without the need—indeed, without the right—to make appraisals and decisions at the local level. We understand there is at least one European country where the Commissioner of Education can look at his calendar and say, "Today all our algebra students will solve the quadratic equation by completing the square." We earnestly hope this never happens in the United States. We do not contemplate the emergence of a national curriculum in mathematics. We think it is far better to inform school officials about all current developments and then to rely on them to initiate studies that will enable them to plan appropriate programs for their pupils.

In this publication we follow the general format of the conferences. First, Professor G. Baley Price talked about *why* change is needed in school mathematics. Dr. Kenneth E. Brown in his address reviewed *what* new materials have been developed. The teacher panelists—four at each of the conferences—discussed their experiences with the new programs. Dr. W. Eugene Ferguson then suggested *how* a school might proceed in establishing a new mathematics program. At the final session the consultants answered questions submitted during the course of the conference, and the Director made a brief closing statement.

In preparing this pamphlet we have avoided technical language in order to make the material accessible to people who are not specially trained in the field of mathematics. At the same time we hope that it will be useful to mathematics teachers who are studying or working in the new programs.

Many people cooperated in the presentation of the Regional Orientation Conferences in Mathematics which made this pamphlet possible. The Director is grateful for the efficient work of the eight Regional Directors; for the guidance and counsel provided by the ten-member Steering Committee; for the distinctive contributions made by the 33 teacher panelists; and for the outstanding performances of Dr. Kenneth E. Brown, Dr. W. Eugene Ferguson, and Professor G. Baley Price as speakers and consultants at these conferences. Special thanks are due Professor Phillip S. Jones, President of the Council, for his advice and encouragement during the course of the conferences; to Mr. M. H. Ahrendt, Executive Secretary, for his efficient handling of the funds provided by the National Science Foundation and for his conscientious supervision of the production of this publication; and to Miss Miriam Goldman, Editorial Associate, for her painstaking work on editorial details.

FRANK B. ALLEN, *Director*
Regional Orientation Conferences in Mathematics

La Grange, Illinois
September, 1961

Table of Contents

I

Progress in Mathematics and Its Implications for the Schools

• G. BALEY PRICE

THE REVOLUTION IN MATHEMATICS

THE CHANGES IN mathematics in progress at the present time are so extensive, so far-reaching in their implications, and so profound that they can be described only as a revolution.

FIRST CAUSE: RESEARCH IN MATHEMATICS

Let us examine the causes of this revolution. It has been caused in the first place by the tremendous advances made by mathematical research. Many members of the general public are surprised to learn that mathematics is a live, active, and growing subject. They seem to feel that mathematics was completed by Newton, and that undergraduate, and even graduate, courses in the subject never change—indeed, that there is no opportunity, need, or occasion for them to change. It is true that if a theorem is once true, it is always true. But theorems, like airplanes, become obsolete because new and better ones are discovered.

The twentieth century has been the golden age of mathematics, since more mathematics, and more profound mathematics, has been created in this period than during all the rest of history. *Mathematical Reviews* is an international abstracting journal that publishes brief reviews of research papers and books; the typical review is about two or three inches long in one column. In spite of the brevity of the reviews, the volume of *Mathematical Reviews* for 1960 contains 1,652 large, double-column pages; and it is estimated that the volume for 1961 will contain 2,400 such pages.

Professor Price is chairman of the Department of Mathematics at The University of Kansas, Lawrence, Kansas. At the time of the conferences he was executive secretary of the Conference Board of the Mathematical Sciences, and during 1961-62 he will continue in this position on a part-time basis.

The present century has seen the introduction and extensive development of subjects in pure mathematics such as abstract algebra, topology, measure theory, general theories of integration, and functional analysis, including the theory of Hilbert space. These subjects were not extensively taught in even the best graduate departments of mathematics until after 1930; as a result, many members of the older generation of mathematicians in the United States did not have courses in these new subjects when they were in graduate school. Since it is impossible to be a mathematician today without a knowledge of these new subjects and their continuing developments, the university mathematician has been forced to continue his "in-service training" throughout his entire career. It would be out of place here to enter into a discussion of the details of the new subjects I have named; it is sufficient to say that the changes made in mathematics by modern research are equally as profound as those in chemistry, physics, and biology.

There has been rapid development in certain other fields of mathematics which are more closely related to important applications than those already named. Probability and statistics are studied not only for their own sake, but also because of their extensive and important applications in the physical and engineering sciences, in the biological sciences, and in the social sciences. The recent development of this field is indicated by the fact that the Institute of Mathematical Statistics was not organized until 1935. The theory of games is a mathematical theory of games of strategy; the history of the subject dates essentially from 1944, when John von Neumann and Oskar Morgenstern published their *Theory of Games and Economic Behavior*. As the title of the book indicates, the theory of games was developed not only for its mathematical interest, but also as a mathematical model in terms of which economic forces and behavior could be explained and understood. Linear programming is usually dated from 1948; it has provided an important tool for the more efficient management of large-scale industrial and governmental operations. Operations research was introduced by England and by the United States to support their war efforts during World War II; after the war, many industrial firms employed operations research methods in an effort to make their operations more efficient and more productive. Operations research employs many mathematical and statistical techniques. The Operations Research Society of America was organized after World War II, and it holds several large national meetings each year. Quality control is concerned with techniques for the efficient control of quality in large-scale manufacturing processes. For example, millions of light bulbs are made by automatic machines; what steps can the manufacturer take to insure that the quality remains at specified levels? There are so many lamp bulbs (and similarly for many other items) that it is not economically feasible to test all of them. Furthermore, a complete test of a lamp bulb (and similarly of other items also) is a destructive test, and only those bulbs that are not tested can be sold. Quality control employs a variety of statistical techniques. The history of the subject dates from 1929 when Walter A. Shewart, of the Bell

Telephone Laboratories, published a book entitled *Economic Control of Quality of Manufactured Product*, but quality control methods and techniques were not widely employed until they were demanded by the necessities of World War II. The field now has its own professional organization, the American Society for Quality Control, which was organized soon after World War II, and now has more than 12,000 members.

SECOND CAUSE: AUTOMATION

Let us return to our original question, namely, what caused the revolution in mathematics? I have said that this revolution was caused first of all by the advances resulting from mathematical research. In the second place, the revolution in mathematics was caused by the automation revolution.

The automation revolution consists of the introduction of machines that control machines, and of the consequences of the use of such machines. Examples of automation abound everywhere. Long distance telephone dialing is a simple but impressive example of automation that is so commonplace that it often passes unappreciated. The automatic pilot that flies our jet airplane is another example of automation. Guided missiles provide still another example. Complicated computers and control mechanisms are required to lift a missile from its launching pad and to place it in orbit. A final example is provided by the computing machines that are programmed to control milling machines for cutting complicated three-dimensional shapes from wood or metal.

The automation revolution has influenced the revolution in mathematics in two ways. First, it has made possible the construction and operation of machines of enormous size, complexity, and cost; and it has thereby created the necessity for the design and development of such machines. Until fairly recent years, most of the design and development problems could be solved by simple experimental procedures. I once heard the late Charles F. Kettering, Director of Research for the General Motors Corporation, explain how to design a better piston ring. He prescribed a simple experimental procedure as follows: "Make several hundred piston rings," he said, "using different combinations of design, metal, finish, and heat treatment. Then put them all in engines and try them out. The piston ring that gives the best performance has the design you want."

I am sure that Mr. Kettering was fully aware of the importance of mathematical and other analytical procedures, but the simple experimental procedures he suggested would undoubtedly be quite successful in the design and development of an item as small and simple as a piston ring. But the typical problem of today does not concern the piston ring, but rather something of the size, complexity, and cost of the B-70 airplane. This plane will be made of stainless steel, and it will be somewhat less than 200 feet long. Its range will be 7,000 miles, and it will fly at 2,000 miles per hour at an altitude of 70,000 feet. It will be capable of carrying in its thirty-foot bays enough nuclear bombs to blow a small nation off the map. Originally, the B-70 program called for 162 planes at a cost of $10 billion, a figure the Senate Preparedness sub-committee said was unrealistically low.[1] The experimental approach outlined by Mr. Kettering would suggest that we build a hundred of the proposed planes, using different combinations of wing types, fuselage designs, engine types and mounts, and control systems. This approach to the problem would be absurd. No test pilot would fly a plane that had been built in this fashion. Everyone knows the design and development of a plane of this type requires that the analysis—much of it mathematical—be carried to such a point that the first one built flies and performs essentially according to specification.

But the automation revolution has influenced the revolution in mathematics in another way. Not only has it created the necessity for solving complicated design and development problems, but it has contributed an important tool for their solution. This tool is so important that I would list it as the third cause of the revolution in mathematics.

THIRD CAUSE: AUTOMATIC DIGITAL COMPUTING MACHINES

The introduction of the large-scale, high-speed, automatic digital computing machine is the third cause of the revolution in mathematics. This computer has made it possible for mathematical theory to be teamed with the computing machine to produce answers that are required by physicists, engineers, and others.

One example will illustrate the change in our ability to compute. About one hundred years ago an Englishman named William Shanks computed π to 707 decimal places. Working with pencil and paper, he devoted 20 years to this undertaking. In 1949, however, the computing machine known as the ENIAC computed π to more than 2,000 decimal places in 70 hours. Furthermore, the modern calculations of π have shown that Shanks made a mistake in the 528th decimal place. Some time after 1949, another machine computed π to more than 3,000 decimal places in 13 minutes. Still later, a smaller machine computed π to 10,000 decimal places; after the result was published in 1957, it was discovered that the machine had made a mistake in the 7,480th decimal place. By 1960, π had been computed correctly to 10,000 decimal places so many times that history does not record all of them.

The importance of the electronic digital computing machine arises not from the fact that certain calculations can be carried out more quickly than heretofore, but rather from the fact that computations which were formerly completely impossible can now be made quickly and efficiently. Consider

---

[1] An article entitled "Program for B-70 at Mock-Up Stage" in the *New York Times* for February 12, 1961, contains the following statement: "Wonder or blunder, more than $797,300,000 has been spent on it so far, and the only tangible product is a wood-metal-plastic contrivance that looks like a cross between a plane and a spaceship."

again the launching of a guided missile. The computing machine remains on the ground, but radar supplies information to it about the flight of the missile. The computing machine makes the necessary calculations and, through a radar connection, sets the controls in the missile. The flight of the missile can be influenced only during the period the engine is in operation, a period which is usually not more than two or three minutes. No group of human computers could possibly receive the data, make the necessary calculations, and transmit the results back to the missile in so few seconds. The electronic digital computer handles the problem with ease.

MATHEMATICS AND THE TECHNOLOGICAL REVOLUTION

The technological revolution now in progress requires that new mathematics be taught in our schools, that the emphasis be shifted in the teaching of many subjects already included in our mathematics courses, and that we increase the production of mathematicians and mathematics teachers.

New Mathematics Required

Several examples will illustrate the changes in the nation's need for mathematics and in the nature of the mathematics courses taught in our schools. In 1850 almost no one was engaged in research. The members of the general public needed to know how to keep simple accounts and how to solve simple problems in measurement. Bookkeeping requires a knowledge of the four operations of arithmetic: addition, subtraction, multiplication, and division. The problems of measurement encountered in 1850 included the determination of the number of acres of land in a field, of the number of cords in a stack of wood, and of the number of bushels of grain in a bin. The public school courses in arithmetic included a treatment of all of these topics.

By the early years of the twentieth century, new needs for mathematics had arisen. I shall now describe one which resulted from two advances in dairy technology. The first advance was the invention and widespread introduction of the cream separator, a machine which separates milk into cream and skim milk; and the second was the development of a simple test for determining the percentage of butterfat in a sample of milk or cream. Given the cream separator and the butterfat test, a common problem for the dairyman is illustrated by the following: How many pounds of milk, testing 5 percent butterfat, and how many pounds of cream, testing 30 percent

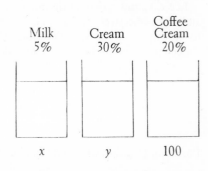

Milk 5%   Cream 30%   Coffee Cream 20%

x y 100

butterfat, must be mixed to give 100 pounds of coffee cream, which tests 20 percent butterfat? Let x and y denote respectively the number of pounds required. Then

$$x + y = 100,$$
$$.05x + .30y = 20.$$

The solution of the problem has led to the solution of two linear equations in two unknowns. For many years high school algebra has included the treatment of the solution of systems of this type.

Next, consider a simple problem in linear programming. A certain manufacturer has warehouses W_1, W_2, and W_3 which contain 100, 200, and 100 tons, respectively, of his product. The manufacturer receives an order for 125 tons of his product from market M_1 and an order for 225 tons from market M_2. The freight rates from the warehouses W_1, W_2, and W_3 to market M_1 are respectively 1, 2, and 3 dollars per ton; and the freight rates from W_1, W_2, and W_3 to M_2 are respectively 6, 5, and 4 dollars per ton. How many tons should the manufacturer ship from each warehouse to each market to fill the two orders?

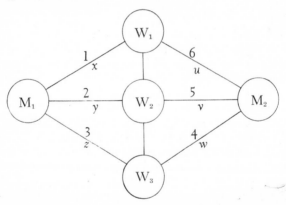

Let x, y, and z denote the number of tons to be shipped from W_1, W_2, and W_3 respectively to M_1; and let u, v, and w denote the number of tons to be shipped from W_1, W_2, and W_3 respectively to M_2. Then from the statement of the problem we obtain the following equations and inequalities:

$$x + y + z = 125,$$
$$u + v + w = 225,$$
$$x + u \leq 100,$$
$$y + v \leq 200,$$
$$x + w \leq 100.$$

Finally, if C denotes the total freight charges for making the shipments, then

$$C = x + 2y + 3z + 6u + 5v + 4w.$$

The solution of the problem is obtained by finding the values of x, y, z, u,

v, and w which satisfy the five equations and inequalities and which give C its minimum value.

Problems of this type are of great practical importance to business, industry, and government. Many examples arise in the oil industry. A given oil company will usually have several sources of crude oil, several refineries, many storage facilities, and widely scattered markets. The problems encountered involve many unknowns, and methods must be devised for solving them on large computing machines.

This problem in linear programming involves considerations which have not been taught in our high school mathematics courses heretofore. These courses have treated linear equations but not linear inequalities. A study of inequalities of all kinds is one of the new topics included in the new mathematics programs for high schools.

Consider the following problem. A certain manufacturer receives an order for 100,000 rods of a certain kind, each of which is to have a diameter of two inches. The buyer knows, however, that it is not economically feasible to produce rods whose diameters are exactly 2.000 inches; accordingly, his order states that rods whose diameters lie between 1.995 inches and 2.005 inches are acceptable. The manufacturer finds that although he cannot

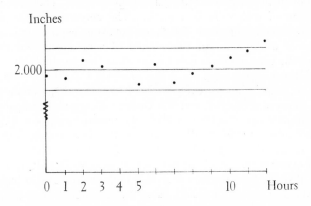

manufacture rods whose diameters are exactly 2.000 inches on an automatic lathe, he can successfully make rods whose diameters lie between 1.995 and 2.005 inches on this lathe. When the cutting tool is dull or when the lathe is out of adjustment, however, the lathe produces rods whose diameters fall outside the specified tolerances. The manufacturer finds that he must institute a quality control procedure to assist him. In a typical procedure a random sample of five rods will be drawn each hour. The diameters of the five rods will be measured and their average will be computed and plotted on a quality control chart. If the average falls within certain limits that have been established for the lathe, the manufacturing process is continued; if it falls outside these limits, the lathe is stopped and put back in proper working order.

The operation of the quality control procedure described is extremely simple, but the mathematics involved in establishing the limits and justifying the procedure includes very deep results in the theory of probability. In the past, probability and statistical inference have not been included in our high school mathematics courses. The Commission on Mathematics, however, considered the subject so important that it wrote a textbook on probability and statistical inference for a course in the second semester of the twelfth grade. Furthermore, the second semester of Contemporary Mathematics, the mathematics course on Continental Classroom, will be devoted to probability and statistical inference, partly because of the importance of this subject for high school teachers, but even more because of its importance for many members of the general public.

Another example will illustrate further the importance of probability and statistics in the everyday affairs of the nation. As mentioned earlier, accounting in the past employed the four fundamental operations of arithmetic; there are strong indications, however, that accounting in the future will involve important applications of probability and statistics.

Consider the telephone companies. A long distance telephone call from New York to San Francisco will use the lines of several different companies, and each of them must receive its share of the revenue. There are undoubtedly millions of such calls each month. The determination of the exact amount of revenue due each telephone company requires only the four operations of arithmetic, but the amount of work involved is enormous. The telephone companies are now investigating the possibility of employing sampling theory in the solution of this problem; the Ohio Public Utilities Commission heard testimony in September 1960 regarding sampling to split revenues between Ohio Bell and the General Telephone Company, which operates in many areas of Ohio. Clearly the total amount of work involved in the accounting will be greatly reduced if the total revenue is divided in the same ratio as that in a small sample of the calls. Important mathematical and legal questions are involved, however. How large should the sample be to insure that the total revenue is divided fairly within certain limits? Will the stockholders accept dividends based on revenues divided by sampling theory methods; will the Bureau of Internal Revenue accept taxes based on income obtained by such methods?

It is freely predicted that sampling theory methods, based on probability and statistical inference, will be widely introduced into accounting procedures in the near future. These developments emphasize once more the importance of probability and statistics for the general public, and the importance of introducing a course on these subjects into the high school curriculum.

CHANGED EMPHASIS IN OLD MATHEMATICS REQUIRED

Thus far I have emphasized the importance of new developments in mathematics. It would be a mistake to believe, however, that the only important parts of mathematics are those which have been discovered and developed recently. Many old subjects are still highly important and we must continue to teach them. Frequently, however, the emphasis must be placed on a different aspect of the subject, and an effort must be made to teach the subject so that the student gains a deeper understanding of it. The teaching of trigonometry and logarithms provides two examples. Trigonometry became a part of the college curriculum in mathematics about 300 years ago when the American colonies were located on the Atlantic seaboard. In the large majority of cases a college graduate became a sea captain, a surveyor, or a minister. A sea captain needed trigonometry for navigation; a surveyor needed it to lay out the farms and cities of the new continent; and the minister needed trigonometry for astronomy and the calculation of the date of Easter. Trigonometry was the all-important applied mathematics of this earlier period, and the solution of triangles was its important aspect.

Today, the important part of trigonometry is the study of the properties of the trigonometric functions rather than the solution of triangles. Radio beams and radar aids have made navigation easy; the new country has been staked out, and only a few, even among the engineers, study surveying; and our observatories now compute the date of Easter. The trigonometric functions, however, have many important applications, for example, in electrical engineering; and trigonometry is still an important subject in applied mathematics if the emphasis is placed on analytic trigonometry rather than on the solution of triangles.

Logarithms were introduced about 300 years ago, and they have been widely taught as an important tool for calculation. But logarithms are no longer important for calculations; small calculations are performed on desk calculators, and large calculations are performed on electronic digital computers. Shall we stop teaching logarithms? Not at all, but the emphasis should be shifted from logarithms as a tool for calculation to a study of the properties of the logarithm function.

Consider a final example. The study of the flow of heat and the distribution of temperatures in a solid body is a problem of great importance at the present time; it was first studied extensively by the French mathematician Jean Fourier early in the nineteenth century. His discoveries had few practical applications at the time, but they have many applications of the highest importance today. Many problems related to the flow of heat occur in the design of every steam power plant, of every air conditioning system, and of every nuclear power plant. The study of the flow of heat, begun by Fourier, and of the mathematical problems which have arisen from this original problem, have had a profound influence on the development of modern mathematics. Some of the changes that are being made in high school mathematics are designed to provide a better foundation for the study of some of the old problems in mathematics and their modern developments. The study of the flow of heat is an advanced problem which cannot be studied in high school. Nevertheless, it is important to develop the points of view and to lay the foundation that will permit the student to understand the old problems and the new methods which have been developed to solve these old problems.

More Mathematicians Required

As a result of the revolution in mathematics, there is an unprecedented demand for mathematicians and mathematics teachers; it is impossible to foresee a time when there will be an adequate supply. This demand for mathematicians is part of a larger demand for highly trained personnel in all fields. This demand represents a long-term development in our civilization—a civilization which is increasingly dependent on scientific and technological advances. This long-term increase in the demand for highly trained personnel was obscured first by the depression of the 1930's and second by the dislocations caused by World War II. The realization of the true situation burst upon the nation with startling suddenness in the 1950's, long after efforts should have been initiated to deal with it.

The Rockefeller Report on Education, entitled *The Pursuit of Excellence*, contains an account of the automation revolution, the accompanying long-term increase in the demand for highly educated personnel, and the crisis that confronts the nation. The following table [2] shows that the percent of the labor force in selected skills and occupations increased from 32.8 percent in 1910 to 47.6 percent in 1957.

Occupational Distribution of Labor Force
(Selected skills and occupations as percent of labor force)

	1910	1957
Professional and technical workers	4.4%	9.9%
Proprietors, managers and officials, excluding farm	6.5	10.3
Clerical workers	10.2	14.1
Skilled workers and foremen	11.7	13.3
Total selected skills and occupations	32.8%	47.6%

The Rockefeller Report on Education stresses the crisis in science and mathematics education in the following paragraphs:[3]

Though we cannot discuss in detail each of the fields of study, it is worthwhile to say a few words about education in science and mathematics. The public reactions to this subject have been so intense and so diverse that it has not been easy

---

[2] From: *The Pursuit of Excellence: Education and the Future of America.* © 1958 by the Rockefeller Brothers Fund, Inc. (as it appears in *Prospect for America*, p. 346. © 1961). Reprinted by permission of Doubleday & Company.

[3] *Ibid.*, p. 368.

for the informed citizen to appraise the issues. The simplest way to avoid confusion is to keep a few basic ideas firmly in mind.

First, the crisis in our science education is not an invention of the newspapers, or scientists, or the Pentagon. It is a real crisis.

Second, the USSR is not the "cause" of the crisis. The cause of the crisis is our breath-taking movement into a new technological era. The USSR has served as a rude stimulus to awaken us to that reality.

The heart of the matter is that we are moving with headlong speed into a new phase of man's long struggle to control his environment, a phase beside which the industrial revolution may appear a modest alteration of human affairs. . . .

How well is our educational system meeting the demands placed upon us? The Rockefeller Report on Education answers as follows: [4]

The fateful question is not whether we have done well, or whether we are doing better than we have done in the past, but whether we are meeting the stern demands and unparalleled opportunities of the times. And the answer is that we are *not*.

A MATHEMATICS EDUCATION ADEQUATE FOR OUR TIMES

The implications of this crisis for our schools are clear. We must put forth whatever effort may be required to insure that the education provided by our schools—and in particular, the mathematics education provided by our schools—is adequate for the needs of our times. I shall now indicate some of the components of the mathematics education that is adequate for our times.

APPROPRIATE COURSE CONTENT

The first component consists of mathematics courses with the proper mathematical content. Many of the topics in such courses are old mathematics, but they are presented in such a way that the student gains greatly increased understanding and insight into the subject. Algebra, an old subject, is one of the central topics in the new courses. Algebra has usually been presented as a collection of rules, which if followed, produce the answer; proofs were reserved entirely for geometry. Algebra in the new courses will now be taught so that its structure—its deductive character—is apparent. Many of the topics in courses with the proper mathematical content concern subjects which are entirely new in the high school curriculum. For example, a chapter on vectors is now available in a mathematics course for the eleventh grade. Vectors form a proper subject for study, not only because they form an interesting new mathematical structure, but also because they have important applications in physics and engineering. Another new topic in the high school curriculum is probability and statistics. I have already mentioned the textbook for a semester course on this subject in the twelfth

---

[4] *Ibid.*, p. 362.

grade. The course has already been taught in a number of high schools and it has been an immediate success everywhere. The engineers, among others, are demanding that their students know more and more about probability, statistics, and their applications. The theory of matrices is a final example of a new mathematical topic in the high school curriculum. Matrices are relatively new in mathematics, being only about a century old; they provide an example of an important new type of algebraic structure, and their study yields a tool of great significance and power in many fields in which mathematics is applied.

QUALIFIED TEACHERS

The second component in mathematics education adequate for our times consists of well-qualified teachers. A teacher must know a great deal of mathematics in order to be a satisfactory teacher of school mathematics. Superintendents and principals should now realize that the day has passed when any teacher who happens to have an otherwise free period can be assigned to teach mathematics. Many of our high school students must now reach a level of attainment expected of college sophomores only 15 or 20 years ago.

The well-qualified teacher must know mathematics, and in addition he must teach the subject with interest and enthusiasm. The high school mathematics teacher must present the elements of algebra, geometry, and trigonometry, but in addition he must preserve and strengthen the student's native interest in and enthusiasm for mathematics. He must make the subject interesting and appealing, so that his pupils will continue to study it with enthusiasm. A teacher who fears and dislikes mathematics will not teach very much mathematics to his students, but he will readily convey his fear and dislike of the subject to many of them. Such a teacher will often build up in his students a permanent fear and dislike of mathematics, and they will abandon the study of the subject at the first opportunity. One of the best ways to attract students to the study of mathematics is to know and like mathematics, and then to teach good, significant courses.

COUNSELORS

The third component in mathematics education adequate for our times consists of counselors who will make certain that those students who have mathematical interests and abilities take at least four years of good mathematics in high school, and that all of those who have the ability to do college work take at least three years of high school mathematics. A student who does not take at least three years of high school mathematics is so handicapped that many fields of study are permanently closed to him when he reaches college. The best courses and the finest teachers are to no avail if students do not take the courses. For this reason, there must be counselors to help students plan their high school programs.

FOUR REQUIREMENTS

I shall now describe four requirements which must be met if our schools are to provide the mathematics education I have described.

IN-SERVICE RETRAINING OF TEACHERS

Many high school mathematics teachers must undertake retraining immediately. Although many teachers had an excellent education originally, they need re-education because of the changes that have taken place in mathematics. Fortunately, excellent opportunities exist. The mathematics course entitled Contemporary Mathematics on NBC's Continental Classroom provides an opportunity for in-service training which is available to most of the teachers in the United States.[5] In addition, many teachers have organized seminars to study the new mathematics in their own schools and thereby gained valuable in-service training. Finally, the National Science Foundation has provided many opportunities for in-service training. Often a teacher can attend an in-service institute operated by a nearby college or university with NSF support. Also, there are many summer and academic-year institutes supported by the National Science Foundation.

BETTER PRE-SERVICE TRAINING OF TEACHERS

A second requirement concerns the training of new teachers. Schools must encourage and help colleges and universities that train teachers to revise their teacher-training programs so that their graduates are adequately prepared to teach the new courses. A vigorous program to modernize teacher-training programs has been launched by the Panel on Teacher Training of the MAA's Committee on the Undergraduate Program in Mathematics. The recommendations of this Panel have been published in the journals of the National Council of Teachers of Mathematics and of the Mathematical Association of America.[6]

IMPROVED TEACHING TECHNIQUES

Next, high school mathematics teachers must re-examine their teaching techniques. Some highly effective new techniques have been introduced by those who have developed the new courses. For example, many teachers have used, with much success, the "discovery technique" of teaching mathematics. Again the School Mathematics Study Group has emphasized the importance of learning mathematics by reading the textbook. SMSG has

---

[5] The National Broadcasting Company announced on June 28, 1961, that Contemporary Mathematics will be repeated from 6 to 6:30 a.m., local time, during 1961-1962.

[6] See "The Training of Elementary School Mathematics Teachers," *The Arithmetic Teacher* 7:421-25; December 1960. See also "Recommendations of the Mathematical Association of America for the Training of Teachers of Mathematics," *The Mathematics Teacher* 8:632-38, 643; December 1960; and *American Mathematical Monthly* 67:982-91; December 1960.

made an important contribution by providing sample textbooks which contain full explanation so that the student can learn by reading his book. It is clear that the introduction of new mathematics into the courses and the development of new teaching techniques have proceeded hand-in-hand.

Sufficiently Large High Schools

A final requirement for the mathematics education which I have described as adequate for our times is that the high school itself be sufficiently large. A small high school cannot provide the mathematics courses and the teachers I have described above as necessary; James B. Conant has suggested that a high school with a graduating class of 100 is the minimum size. Students in a smaller school almost certainly are denied proper mathematics courses. The nation cannot waste its limited supply of good mathematics teachers by placing them in schools where they teach their specialty to less than full capacity. The nation cannot afford the waste of talent that results from sending gifted students (they occur also in small schools!) to schools with poor mathematics programs and poor teachers. Fortunately, many states are solving the problem of the small high school by consolidating small schools into large schools.

*   *   *

In conclusion, I must emphasize that the elementary school, the junior high school, and the senior high school lay the foundation. I must emphasize that the elementary school teacher, the junior high school teacher, and the senior high school teacher are absolutely essential to the success of our program to provide better mathematics; for these teachers must teach mathematics; and these teachers must teach with enthusiasm so that their students continue the study of mathematics.

2

The Drive To Improve
School Mathematics

• KENNETH E. BROWN

"I CHALLENGE the United States to competition in education," said the USSR Deputy Minister of Education to the US delegation at an international conference on the teaching of mathematics, July 1956, in Geneva. Why was this challenge issued with such confidence? Perhaps it was because the USSR representative realized that mathematics is the cornerstone to technical advancement, and that while the USSR was planning to develop the mathematics potential of every high school pupil, the United States had no such plan.

Mathematicians and teachers, however, are now trying to improve high school mathematics courses in this country. In this report I shall discuss the new, improved programs.

NEW USES FOR MATHEMATICS

I believe that the recent marvelous achievements in space are not due to the cold war tensions; they simply reflect our fast-moving society. The balloon carrying an electronics laboratory, the flying box with a dying dog, and the man orbiting the earth in a space capsule are symbols of the great explosion of knowledge that has taken place in our generation.

Contributing substantially to these advances are new uses for mathematics and recently-developed mathematics. Chemists and physicists have found new uses and interpretations for mathematics; biologists are applying mathematics to the study of genetics; businessmen are using mathematics in scheduling production and distribution; and sociologists are using complicated statistical ideas. Even game theory has important applications to hu-

Dr. Brown is specialist for mathematics at the Office of Education, U. S. Department of Health, Education, and Welfare, Washington, D. C.

man behavior, and mathematical models give promise as a basis for the interpretation of phenomena in many disciplines. Indeed, mathematics has become the basic fabric of our social order. The strength of that fabric—in fact the very survival of our Nation—may well depend upon the amount and kind of mathematics taught in our high schools. This is a great and sobering responsibility for those who design and administer the programs. If we take this responsibility lightly, our children will suffer the consequences of our foolish inaction.

While high school enrollments have gone up over the years, the percent of student time spent on mathematics has declined. The new programs we shall discuss and the counseling activities mentioned by Professor Price are aimed at encouraging students—particularly those with special aptitudes in this area—to learn more mathematics and to prolong their study of mathematics. In our increasingly technical age this is important not only to students who want to be mathematicians and scientists, but, as we have suggested, it is important to students preparing for many other occupations.

FINANCIAL AID FOR CURRICULUM IMPROVEMENT

Recognizing the vital need to improve school mathematics programs, national foundations have contributed large sums of money for experimentation in this area. While the foundations do not aim at the development of a national curriculum in high school mathematics, they contribute generously to experimentation that helps local schools secure better mathematics programs. The Carnegie Foundation, for example, has given $500,000 to one center of experimentation.

The Federal Government expects local school systems to plan and develop their own high school mathematics programs, but it considers improvement so important that through the National Science Foundation it has contributed more than $4 million to the School Mathematics Study Group for the development of sample textbooks. These books do not present a national curriculum; rather it is hoped that the material will serve as a guide to authors and to school systems attempting to improve their own programs.

Several other foundations, recognizing the urgent need, have provided financial assistance to help mathematicians and teachers accelerate needed changes.

IMPROVED MATHEMATICS PROGRAMS

Let us look at some of the improved mathematics programs now in progress. For sources of information and experimental material on new programs in arithmetic at the elementary school level, see page 72. We shall confine our discussion here to high school programs.

There are many similarities among the different programs, but there are

The table below shows the grades for which material is now available from some of the improved programs.

| | Textbooks Available | | | | | |
	7th	8th	9th	10th	11th	12th
SMSG	x	x	x	x	x	x
UICSM (Univ. of Illinois)			x	x	x	
Univ. of Southern Ill.			x	x		
Ball State T. C.		x	x	x		
Boston Series		x				
University of Maryland	x	x				

also differences—both in development and in emphasis. One program may have involved many more persons in its development than another; one program may have been tried in many cities in the United States and another confined to a local region; one program may have material for grades 7 through 12 and another for only some of these grades; one program may emphasize the discovery method and another the historical approach. We shall discuss some of the similarities after brief descriptions of the history and the work of those high school programs that now have material available to the public. Sources of current information about these programs are listed on page 87.

School Mathematics Study Group

The School Mathematics Study Group (SMSG) represents the largest united effort for improvement in the history of mathematics education. It is national in scope. The director is Professor E. G. Begle, whose office was, until recently, at Yale University (probably the reason it is sometimes referred to as the *Yale Project*). In the fall of 1961 Professor Begle and SMSG headquarters moved to Stanford University, Palo Alto, California. SMSG is financed by the National Science Foundation.

The development of the SMSG material is unique in that it represents the combined thinking of many people—psychologists, testmakers, mathematicians from colleges and industry, biologists, and high school teachers. Approximately 100 mathematicians and 100 high school teachers did the writing, and in order to produce material that is both mathematically sound and teachable, each writing team had an equal number from each group.

During the school year 1959-60 sample textbooks and teachers' manuals for grades 7 through 12 were tried out in 45 states by more than 400 teachers and 42,000 pupils. During this tryout the teachers received guidance and consultative assistance from college mathematicians.

Throughout the year detailed evaluations of each chapter of the sample textbooks were submitted by teachers, mathematics advisers, and in some cases by the pupils themselves. All the suggestions and criticisms were studied and analyzed by the revision writing team composed of approximately 50 high school teachers and 50 mathematicians. The revision team made many changes—sharpening the discussion, giving better choice of graded exercises, and rewriting certain troublesome spots. They also rewrote those areas identified by the pupils as especially troublesome or difficult. Despite these revisions, it is significant that no changes were suggested in the basic mathematics or philosophy of the original material.

The SMSG textbooks contain new topics as well as changes in the organization and presentation of older topics. Attention is focused on important mathematical facts and skills and on basic principles that provide a logical framework for them. Some of these texts are described as follows in the SMSG *Newsletter No. 4* (March 1960):

Mathematics for Junior High School
Volumes I and II.

Emphasized in these texts are the following important ideas of junior high school mathematics: structure of arithmetic from an algebraic viewpoint; the real number system as a progressing development; metric and non-metric relations in geometry. These ideas are constantly associated with their applications. Time is given to the topics of measurement and elementary statistics. Careful attention is paid to the appreciation of abstract concepts, the role of definition, development of precise vocabulary and thought, experimentation, and proof. Materials are chosen with the intent to capture the fascinating features of mathematics, creation and discovery, rather than just utility alone. . . .

First Course in Algebra

This text emphasizes the structure of algebra. The study of algebra is based on the exploration of the behavior of numbers. Careful attention is paid to the language of the subject. . . .

Intermediate Mathematics

. . . . Careful attention has been taken to give the student some insight into the nature of mathematical thought as well as to prepare him to perform certain manipulations with facility. . . . The text continues in the vein of the ninth-grade material, in that structure is emphasized at all times. . . .

The word *structure* appears frequently in the SMSG descriptions; we shall discuss this concept later.

Solid geometry is not presented by SMSG as a separate course; it is introduced early in tenth grade geometry to help develop the student's space perception. In some cases the formal proofs in solid geometry are integrated with plane geometry, and in other cases they are presented in special chapters. Algebra and geometry are frequently integrated. While intuitive insight is encouraged, emphasis is placed on exact statements of definitions and theorems.

SMSG textbooks and detailed teachers' manuals for grades 7 through 12, as well as several enrichment pamphlets, are now available. The SMSG

Newsletter, with periodic progress reports and descriptions of materials produced, is distributed without charge to those asking to be placed on the mailing list.

University of Illinois Curriculum Study in Mathematics

The University of Illinois Curriculum Study in Mathematics (UICSM) is a joint effort, under the direction of Dr. Max Beberman, by the College of Education, the College of Engineering, and the College of Liberal Arts and Sciences at the University of Illinois. The project is sponsored by the Carnegie Corporation of New York and the University of Illinois. At present UICSM has textbooks for grades 9, 10, and 11; texts for grade 12 will be available in 1962. The textbooks emphasize consistency, precision of language, structure of mathematics, and understanding of basic principles through pupil discovery. Discovery of generalizations by the student is a basic technique used throughout the course.

Work on the UICSM material began in 1952, and by the end of the 1959-60 school year the material had been used experimentally in 25 states by 200 teachers and 10,000 pupils. Participating teachers have received detailed instructions on the use of this experimental material from the Illinois Center.

University of Maryland Mathematics Project

The University of Maryland Mathematics Project (UMMaP), under the direction of Dr. John R. Mayor, was designed to develop an improved mathematics program for grades 7 and 8. Five mathematicians and approximately 40 teachers took part in planning and/or writing the experimental program, with consultative services from specialists in such other areas as psychology and testing.

Although the original experiment was confined primarily to nearby schools (Prince Georges and Montgomery Counties, Maryland; Arlington County, Virginia; and the District of Columbia), the books have now been used in ten states by about 100 teachers with 5,000 pupils. The seventh grade textbook has been revised three times, and the eighth grade textbook, twice.

The courses are designed to serve as a bridge between arithmetic and high school mathematics. Unusual chapter titles such as the following appear in the seventh grade textbook: "Systems of Numeration," "Symbols," "Properties of Natural Numbers," "Factoring and Primes," "The Numbers One and Zero," "Mathematical Systems," "Scientific Notation for Arithmetic Numbers," "Logic and Number Sentences."

Boston College Mathematics Institute

The Boston College Mathematics Institute, under the supervision of Rev. Stanley J. Bezuszka, S.J., will eventually provide material for grades 8 through 12. An experimental textbook for grade 9 was completed, but it was found to be more suitable for grade 8. Another text for grade 9 is now being prepared.

Historical development is used to break away from the traditional approach as well as to give the pupil an opportunity to exercise his imagination and creativity and to encourage him to do some reading. Mathematics is studied through problems that confronted primitive man and questions currently being answered by mathematicians. The emphasis is on the structure of mathematics approached from the historical point of view.

BALL STATE TEACHERS COLLEGE EXPERIMENTAL PROGRAM

The Ball State Teachers College Experimental Program, initiated under the direction of Dr. Charles Brumfiel, is planned for pupils in grades 7 through 12. (Dr. Brumfiel, now at the University of Michigan, is still active in the project.) The program emphasizes the axiomatic structure of mathematics and precision of language. As a result of experimentation at the Ball State Laboratory School, Muncie, Indiana, materials for grades 8, 9, and 10 have gone through several revisions. The books, *Introduction to Mathematics, Algebra I,* and *Geometry,* are now being published by Addison-Wesley Publishing Company, Reading, Massachusetts. The texts are characterized by careful attention to logical development. Both the algebra and the geometry contain carefully constructed chapters on elementary logic. These chapters appear early in the texts, and the ideas developed in them are utilized continually in both courses.

DEVELOPMENTAL PROJECT IN SECONDARY MATHEMATICS
SOUTHERN ILLINOIS UNIVERSITY

The Developmental Project in Secondary Mathematics at Southern Illinois University, under the direction of Professors Morton R. Kenner and Dwain E. Small, receives financial assistance from the Marcell M. Holzer Fund for Education. The program emphasizes the structure of mathematics and precision of language. The language of sets and the axioms of mathematics stand out in the ninth grade textbook. The ninth and tenth grade materials have been tried out in the University High School. Materials for other secondary school grades are being developed.

COMMISSION ON MATHEMATICS
COLLEGE ENTRANCE EXAMINATION BOARD

In the spring of 1959 the Commission on Mathematics of the College Entrance Examination Board issued a 2-part report (Part I: *Program for College Preparatory Mathematics;* Part 2: *Appendices*) on the secondary mathematics curriculum for college-bound students. In this report the Commission recommends revision of the present high school mathematics program to emphasize deductive reasoning in algebra, structure in mathematics, unifying ideas, and treatment of inequalities, and to incorporate some coordinate geometry; a suggested sequence of topics for the high school curriculum is also included. The report may be obtained by writing the Commission on Mathematics, College Entrance Examination Board, c/o Educational Testing Service, Princeton, New Jersey.

THE SECONDARY SCHOOL CURRICULUM COMMITTEE
NATIONAL COUNCIL OF TEACHERS OF MATHEMATICS

The Secondary School Curriculum Committee, under the direction of Frank B. Allen, was appointed by the National Council of Teachers of Mathematics to study mathematics curriculum and instruction in secondary schools in relation to the needs of contemporary society. Eleven subcommittees were formed to make studies and reports in the following areas:

1. The place of mathematics in a changing society.
2. The aims of mathematics education and the pedagogy of mathematics.
3. The nature of mathematical thought for grades 7 through 12.
4. How geometry should be introduced and developed.
5. The content and organization of junior high school mathematics.
6. Foreign mathematics programs for pupils of ages 12 through 18.
7. Adjustment of the mathematics program to pupils of average and below-average ability.
8. Aids to teaching.
9. Organization of the mathematics program.
10. The administration of the mathematics program.
11. Mathematics for academically gifted pupils.

The subcommittee findings were incorporated in a report first published in the May 1959 issue of *The Mathematics Teacher* and subsequently reprinted as a separate publication. This reprint may be obtained from the National Council of Teachers of Mathematics.

The committee studies also resulted in the publication of the following three pamphlets by the NCTM: *A Guide to the Use and Procurement of Teaching Aids for Mathematics*, by Emil J. Berger and Donovan A. Johnson; *Mathematics Tests Available in the United States*, by Sheldon S. Myers; and *The Supervisor of Mathematics, His Role in the Improvement of Mathematics Instruction*, by Veryl Schult.

SIMILARITIES OF THE NEW PROGRAMS

One might think, on learning about the various new programs in mathematics, that the profession is behaving like Stephen Leacock's Lord Ronald, who flung himself upon his horse and rode madly off in all directions at once. This is not the case. While each program has unique features, all share common elements and all are aimed at the improvement of mathematics instruction.

Unifying Themes in Mathematics

All the programs we have discussed attempt to avoid the presentation of new material as a string of unrelated topics. Indeed, they stress unifying themes or ideas in mathematics [1] such as the following:

Structure
Operations and their inverses
Measurement
Extensive use of graphical representation
Systems of numeration
Properties of numbers, development of the real number system
Statistical inference, probability
Sets—language and elementary theory
Logical deductions
Valid generalizations.

Set Theory

Many high school pupils have seen mathematics as a series of separate and unrelated manipulative tricks. The improved programs, on the other hand, have tried to use as central themes the permeating ideas in mathematics. In some cases this has led to the introduction of words and ideas from college mathematics.

Set theory, for example, is a unifying idea found in higher mathematics; however, it is simple enough in its beginnings to be taught in high school.

DEFINITION: A *set* is any well-defined collection of distinguishable objects of our perception or thought. For instance:

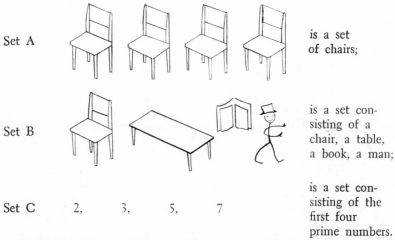

Set A .... is a set of chairs;

Set B .... is a set consisting of a chair, a table, a book, a man;

Set C   2,   3,   5,   7   is a set consisting of the first four prime numbers.

Once the notion of set is introduced, it may be used throughout the course. The student refers to solution sets of equations, truth sets, sets of

---

[1] A comprehensive discussion of unifying ideas appears in the 24th Yearbook of the National Council of Teachers of Mathematics: *The Growth of Mathematical Ideas, Grades K-12*. This book may be purchased from the NCTM.

ordered pairs, etc. He is given exercises to strengthen and clarify his idea of sets before any symbols are used. He will use these symbols and terminology in more advanced mathematics, and the ideas will be further developed as he takes additional courses.

STRUCTURE

Another area of emphasis common to all the improved programs is *structure*. It is reflected in the careful development of mathematics as a deductive system. Since the phrase *structure of mathematics* is used frequently in the improved programs, we should consider its meaning. The study of the structure of mathematics is the study of the basic principles or properties common to all systems of mathematics. These systems, in fact, may not even be concerned with numbers.

Let us try a few simple analogies. In the development of counting, man referred to two ducks as a brace of ducks, two oxen as a yoke of oxen, two doves as a pair of doves. Many other terms were used for two specific things. The big generalization came when man observed that there was something all these combinations had in common—*two*. The number two is a mathematical abstraction of which two sheep, two horses, two oxen, are concrete manifestations. It is through the study of such abstractions that we gain an understanding of the structure of mathematics.

The expression "$3 \times 5 = 15$" is an abstract mathematical idea that can be applied to finding the cost of 3 pencils at 5¢ each or the area of a rug 3 yards by 5 yards. The abstract idea may be likened to the structure of mathematics, and the applications are the models to which the abstract system is applied. There has been a tendency in high school to look at the characteristics or properties of each model separately. This tendency has resulted in the students' learning many seemingly unrelated rules. A study of the structure of mathematical systems has led to fewer rules or properties.

To clarify further the idea of structure of a mathematical system, let us look at Figure 1. In the body of the table are the symbols O and E. In one corner of the table is another symbol, +. We shall let O represent any *odd*

+	O	E
O	E	O
E	O	E

Fig. 1

number and E represent any *even* number. The symbol + indicates the operation of addition. If we perform the operation on the O at the left with the O at the top, we obtain the E in the second line: O (odd number) + O (odd number) = E (even number). If the O at the left is paired with the E at the top we get the O in the second line: O (odd number) + E (even number) = O (odd number). If we study the table we see that:

$$O + E = O$$
$$E + E = E$$

Since we do not change either O or E by adding E to it, the element E is called the identity element with respect to addition, or simply the additive identity. In arithmetic the identity element for addition is zero. A number plus zero equals that same number:

$$N + 0 = N$$
$$4 + 0 = 4$$

Returning to the table, we may observe that:

$$O + E = O$$
$$E + O = O$$
$$\text{or } O + E = E + O$$

Since the order of adding the two numbers does not affect the sum, we have demonstrated the commutative property of addition. In arithmetic an example is $4 + 3 = 3 + 4$.

There are many other properties that could be demonstrated for this table, but let us keep in mind the existence of the additive identity and the commutative property of addition.

In Figure 2 we again have two symbols in the body of the table and a sign of operation in the corner. A means that an object is turned half way around (180°) and B means the object is turned clear around (360°). The → shows the order. For example, A → B = A means the object is first turned 180° and then turned 360°, leaving the object in the same position as if turned 180°.

→	A	B
A	B	A
B	A	B

Fig. 2

Let us note what happens when we reverse the order of the turns:

$$A \rightarrow B = A$$
$$B \rightarrow A = A$$
$$\text{or } A \rightarrow B = B \rightarrow A$$

We see, then, that the order does not affect the result—a half turn followed by a full turn leaves the object in the same position as a full turn followed by a half turn, and we know that the commutative property applies for this operation.

We also observe that:

$$A \to B = A$$
$$B \to B = B$$

or that B has the identity property. In this case A and B do not represent numbers, and the operation represented by $\to$ is not one in arithmetic.

In Figure 3 we again have two symbols in the table and a sign of operation in the corner. In this case the symbols, $\triangle$ and $\bigcirc$, represent two different

$\to$	$\triangle$	$\bigcirc$
$\triangle$	$\bigcirc$	$\triangle$
$\bigcirc$	$\triangle$	$\bigcirc$

Fig. 3

abstract ideas; they do not represent horses or dollars. The $\to$ represents a rule that is expressed in the table. That is, if $\triangle$ is paired with $\triangle$ we get $\bigcirc$ which we shall write as $\triangle \to \triangle = \bigcirc$.

A study of the table reveals:

$$\triangle \to \bigcirc = \triangle$$
$$\bigcirc \to \triangle = \triangle$$
$$\text{or } \triangle \to \bigcirc = \bigcirc \to \triangle$$

The order of operation does not affect the result, and this operation has the commutative property.

Also we see that:

$$\bigcirc \to \bigcirc = \bigcirc$$
$$\triangle \to \bigcirc = \triangle$$

If the circle is used with the circle we get the circle; if it is used with the triangle we get the triangle. The circle, then, is the identity element with respect to this operation.

Let us consider all three figures: Figure 1 is concerned with numbers, Figure 2 is concerned with moving an object, and Figure 3 is concerned with abstract ideas. All three have two properties in common. What does this have to do with the structure of mathematics? Figure 3 represents a miniature mathematical system; Figures 1 and 2 are models or applications of the system.

For many years high school mathematics has consisted of the study of the models, and pupils have failed to see the basic properties common to all. In the improved programs the pupils look at the mathematical system itself. The properties of the abstract system, Figure 3, apply to the models. Properties, in fact, may be obvious in the abstract system that are hidden by the physical objects in the models. The properties of the mathematical system are fundamental and enduring; the models or applications change as the needs of our society change.

MEASUREMENT

Measurement is another unifying concept that appears throughout the improved programs. The importance of a standard, well-defined unit is common knowledge on the elementary level. Elementary school pupils are asked to measure with sticks of their own choosing to help them understand that in order to communicate they must have a standard unit. Each child must know the meaning of such measurements as 1 foot or 1 pint.

In high school at times we have assumed the pupil knew what we meant by the measure of an angle or the distance between P and Q. This is not the case in the improved programs. For example, in the SMSG ninth grade textbook the meaning of the distance PQ is carefully discussed. In the tenth grade the pupil studies a chapter entitled "Measurement of Distance." In the eleventh grade this concept is again considered, but on a higher level.

SYSTEMS OF NUMERATION

Other systems of numeration are frequently studied in the improved programs to develop a better understanding of our own system. For example, our counting numbers may be expressed with only two symbols, such as 1 and 0, instead of all the symbols from 0 to 9. If we have a device that responds to the flow of electricity through a wire so that when the current is on it represents 1, and when the current is off it represents 0, then our device performs addition with *two* symbols rather than *ten*. This system of numeration is used in many electronic computers. Pupils may practice adding and multiplying in the system—not to attain proficiency for operating a computer but to gain a better understanding of the decimal system of numeration.

OPERATIONS

The meaning of operations is stressed in the new programs. Addition and multiplication are given as the basic operations; subtraction and division are simply inverse operations of multiplication and addition. The stress is on "why you perform the operation as you do" rather than "this is the way to do it." Analogies are used less and basic reasons more. In the improved programs the pupil is not told that $7a + 3a = 10a$ because 7 horses + 3 horses = 10 horses. Indeed, after proper introduction to the distributive principle he need not be told. He knows that $7a + 3a = (7 + 3)a$. In the new programs we do not tell students that one cannot add $3a$ and $3b$ because one cannot add 3 horses and 3 cows. This approach creates confusion when, a few weeks later, the student is asked to multiply $3a$ and $3b$ and the "horses and cows" analogy breaks down.

Manipulation without understanding is discouraged in the improved programs; a clear understanding of operations is one of the major goals of all these programs.

LOGICAL DEDUCTIONS

The improved mathematics programs encourage pupils to make correct generalizations by emphasizing "if-then" relationships. If A is true, then by logical reasoning B is or is not true. Following are examples of problems designed to bring forth such generalizations:

Consider several triangles ABC. How does AB + BC compare with AC? AB + AC compare with BC? The responses suggest a general conclusion. If you think this conclusion is true for all triangles, write it as a proposition. This, of course, requires the use of the "if-then" form.

Suppose you have 240 square patio stones (flagstones). You can arrange them in rows to form a variety of rectangular floors for a patio. If s represents the number of stones in a row and n represents the number of rows, then what are the possibilities?

GRAPHICAL REPRESENTATION

The improved programs use graphs to help the pupils see relationships. A line graph may be used to show the relation between two numbers such as 3 and its opposite, −3, or a graph may be used to picture the relationship expressed in an equation or inequality. Observe the graphs in Figure 4. They are, of course, presented at different stages in the pupil's learning of mathematics.

VALID GENERALIZATIONS

In the improved programs the material progresses from concrete examples to abstract symbols; there is an attempt to present patterns or structure in mathematics, and new ideas are related to English sentences. In the University of Illinois program a special emphasis is placed on discovery; the teacher leads the pupil in discovering the basic principles of mathematics.

                    *   *   *   *

We have reviewed some common elements of the programs to improve school mathematics, and we have seen that they are not entirely different from one another. Earlier we discussed some of the differences in development and emphasis. It would appear that there are more points of similarity than of difference.

EFFECTS OF THE NEW PROGRAMS

The improved programs have not been in operation long enough to permit a statistical evaluation. However, the available data show that pupils in the

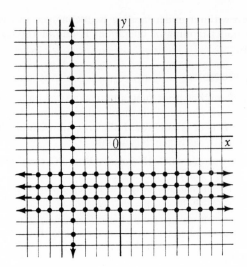

$x = -4$ or $-7 < y < -2$, where x and y are integers

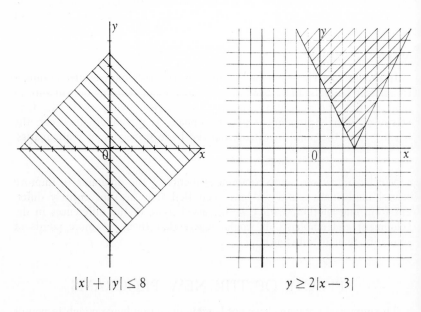

$|x| + |y| \leq 8$

$y \geq 2|x - 3|$

Fig. 4

improved programs do as well as other pupils on traditional tests and also learn more of the basic principles that underlie all of mathematics.

Test makers, responding to the need to improve school mathematics, are keeping pace with the changes that are taking place. Following are several sample items furnished by a national testing organization which reflect recent changes in the teaching of mathematics:

Which of the following properties is (are) applicable to both the set of integers and the set of rational numbers?

I. Between any two of the set there is a third.
II. There is a least positive member of the set.
III. There is a greatest number of the set.
IV. There is an additive inverse for each element in the set.

The symbol ∩ represents the intersection of two sets and the symbol ∪ represents the union of two sets. Which of the following represents the shaded portion of the Venn diagram below?

(A)   (X ∩ Y) ∪ Z

(B)   X ∪ (Y ∩ Z)

(C)   X ∩ (Y ∪ Z)

(D)   (X ∩ Y) ∩ Z

(E)   (X ∪ Y) ∩ Z

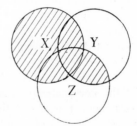

How many numbers in the set $\{-5, -3, 0, 3\}$ satisfy both of the conditions $|n - 3| \leq 6$, and $|n + 2| < 5$?

(A) None   (B) One   (C) Two   (D) Three   (E) Four

The number of points in the intersection of the graph of $|x| = |y|$ and the graph of $|x| + |y| = 1$ is

(A) 0   (B) 1   (C) 2   (D) 3   (E) 4

The improved programs are considered by many mathematicians and high school teachers to be the mathematics of most worth. And teachers who have used these materials have approved wholeheartedly. Many of them testify that the pupils can do the mathematics and enjoy it.

The drive to improve school mathematics is under way; the general pattern is clear, and the necessary materials of instruction are at hand. School administrators are now in a position to lead their teachers in establishing programs of instruction which will raise the level of mathematical competence of their pupils. This important and urgent task must be accomplished.

3

Classroom Experiences with the New Mathematics Programs

THE REGIONAL ORIENTATION CONFERENCES gave school officials the opportunity to meet and talk with teachers who have presented new mathematics materials in the classroom. Do these teachers believe that the new programs are superior? If so, why? How have their supervisors and principals helped them to get started? What results have been achieved? How have students reacted? What seems to be the prevailing attitude among the parents of these students? At each regional conference such questions were discussed by a panel consisting of four teachers who had successfully taught some of the new materials. Each teacher gave a short talk describing his own experiences with one of the new programs. Following the talks there was a question session of about an hour. All who heard the teachers were impressed with their enthusiasm for the new programs and their willingness to work hard to achieve the superior results made possible by the new materials.

On the following pages we attempt, through the use of suitably chosen quotations, to convey some of the ideas and opinions so well expressed by our teacher panelists. Each quotation we have included was made with reference to a particular program but each is, nonetheless, similar to many statements made about other programs. By emphasizing the common elements and the common problems encountered in establishing *any* new program we seek to outline the wealth of useful information provided by our 33 teacher panelists.[1]

The understanding and support of the school administration are essential for the success of the new programs. All the teacher panelists expressed appreciation for the guidance and encouragement provided by supervisory and administrative personnel in their schools. Typical comments:

---

[1] The teacher panelists are listed in the Appendix, pages 89-90.

► I had the advantage of a progressive, cooperative principal who wanted to incorporate some new mathematics into the junior high school program.

► It is interesting that both our headmaster and assistant headmaster were former math teachers. Needless to say, they were vitally interested in our new mathematics curriculum.

* * *

Orientation meetings with faculty and with parent groups can do much to eliminate misunderstanding and unfounded criticism.

► Education in the new program must take place at three levels:

    A. The teacher and his associates must receive appropriate training.

    B. The parents must be convinced that we're still teaching mathematics.

    C. The students must be converted, but they are the easiest to convert.

► I think criticism was to be expected. We are human beings with a natural tendency to question the new until it has been proved; and, after all, this is a desirable trait. We learn by experience, and I now believe that most of the criticism could have been prevented by an explanation in the beginning to the faculty concerning the plan and purposes of the program.

► Usually a short talk with parents is effective; in fact, the whole problem resolves itself into one of communication. PTA meetings offer a convenient medium for reaching a large number of parents at one time. We have found that parents are often impressed with the caliber of the people who have produced these texts; they do not seem to be the type who would try to swindle the public.

* * *

A teacher's reaction to one of these new programs is very likely to depend on how well he is prepared to teach it.

► Teachers with strong backgrounds for the experimental programs are enthusiastic about them.

► Teachers with weak backgrounds have mixed reactions. They experience some doubts and frustrations. Most of them, however, feel that as they develop the particular skills and understandings required they will be able to teach the experimental material more effectively than the traditional material of the past.

► The stronger the teacher's background, the more enthusiastic he becomes about this program.

* * *

All agree that those who are teaching one of the new programs for the first time will have to do a considerable amount of extra work.

► I have never worked harder to keep ahead of my students, but I have never enjoyed a year more.

► No one can remain a "rocking-chair teacher" when the challenge comes. It is not a program which can be taught by the 8:30 to 3:30 teacher.

* * *

One reason experienced teachers have to work so hard on the new programs is that they, unlike their students, have a great deal to unlearn.

► Teachers who have extensive experience with the traditional program often find it difficult to shed the familiar garments.

► In general, the teachers who have taught in our experimental program have faced greater problems of adjustment than have the students.

*   *   *

Those who have taught the improved programs would not return to the traditional texts.

► As I improved I became more enthusiastic, and today I find it impossible to teach the traditional text.

► After spending the summer with a group of 50 teachers and comparing experiences with them, I feel fortunate that I am not teaching in a state and a system that require the use of one of a small group of state-adopted texts or the use of the same book for five years before a new text is selected. I should be very unhappy if, for some reason, I were now required to go back to teaching from a conventional textbook.

*   *   *

Student response to the new programs, as seen by the teachers, is mainly favorable.

► Some of the students who had considered conventional mathematics dull and uninteresting came to life after exposure to the new materials and performed splendidly. The weak students found it difficult to follow the patterns of precise logical reasoning, although tests proved that they did as well with this material as they had done with the traditional materials.

► Students who had gone unnoticed before were thrilled because for once they were allowed to ask "off-beat" questions or to disagree with accepted reasons for doing things. They were allowed to find the answers for themselves.

► I had expected the new and strange vocabulary to present a very difficult problem, but the students use such words as *commutative, associative, distributive, multiplicative identity,* and *additive inverse* with a great deal of ease, and they enjoy doing it. It seems that if they first understand an idea, the vocabulary used to name it presents no difficulty. The precise vocabulary of the course helps to clarify many mathematical ideas.

► You must interest adolescents in the mathematical ideas themselves. It is of little value to try to obtain student interest by promises of utility in adult life. Most high school students are not genuinely stirred by such sales campaigns. The goal of educational utility is too remote to make much difference to a ninth grader. He wants to know how mathematics fits into his world. And, happily, his world is full of fancy and abstractions. Thus students become interested in mathematics because it gives them quick access to a kind of intellectual adventure that is enticing and satisfying.

► The part of the course that has given the greatest amount of trouble is the part most closely resembling the work they have done before.

► I'll tell you why they are more interested. These SMSG texts give them a chance to think about mathematics, to discuss mathematics, and to argue about mathematics. When I visit some classes that are using these texts, especially seventh grade, I find spirited arguments going on, and this is a good sign that some learning is going on too. These texts give the student little chance to become bored with routine. Just as he thinks the problems have settled down and are all susceptible to the same method of solution, up pops something different.

*   *   *

The student's reaction also depends on his ability and previous training. However, this does not mean that slow students dislike the new programs.

► Capable students who receive moderately competent instruction are usually enthusiastic about the course. It has been particularly gratifying to see several brilliant students who had found conventional mathematics dull and uninteresting come to life and perform magnificently after exposure to the new materials.

► Weak students who cannot follow patterns of precise logical reasoning seem to perform as well in the experimental courses as in traditional courses. Their attitudes toward the experimental courses seem little different from the attitudes of weak students toward conventional mathematics courses.

► Within the group of average students there is considerable variation. Many rise to the challenge and do beautiful work. Others passively resist attempts to arouse their interest, refuse to work hard, and perform poorly. Clearly, the central ideas of the geometry and algebra are not inaccessible to the high school student of average ability who is reasonably well motivated and has good work habits.

► At junior high level I have had some of my most interesting classes among really slow students with whom I discussed very abstract ideas.

► The big thrill with the University of Maryland material came when the average student rose to the challenge and did beautiful work.

► The student who is below average in ability shows the same kind of interest that he has always shown. In my opinion the Ball State mathematics program does an excellent job with upper-ability and average-ability students. It offers them the opportunity to learn to reason logically, to learn concepts—to learn the *why* of mathematics. The below-average student gets along about the same, it seems to me, and the Ball State program certainly does not harm him; he will still be able to read a water meter and sharpen his pencil. I do want to stress that the Ball State program is definitely not uninterested in the poor student—nor does it ignore the need for reading of water meters. The program is merely an attempt to teach mathematics—something we have not been doing as well as we could have.

► My class was an unselected group with the majority of IQ's in the average range. To my surprise most of the students comprehended very well the concepts presented. They were intensely interested, even to the point of excitement.

► At the beginning of my discussion, I mentioned the problem of the slow child. Students who have previously made low grades because of lack of interest rather than lack of ability tend to profit by this course. After experimenting with heterogeneous groups, however, I question the wisdom of placing students who are actually low in ability in the course at this time. It is probably true that they will get as much from this as from the traditional course, but neither they nor their parents think that they do.

► The slower student, one who comes to rely on memory to get him through, may have more difficulty with these texts than with standard ones. Even so, it is not impossible that he may be more interested at the same time.

*   *   *

Teachers had solicited students' views of the new mathematics. Following are unsigned student appraisals which were collected and read by the teacher after the grades were turned in.

► The main purpose of Ball State geometry is not to have us memorize a volume of facts, but to help us learn the processes of reasoning in order that we may be able to answer problems we have never seen before. . . . Although I have found it difficult, I believe that I'm progressing toward the understanding of plane geometry in particular and mathematics in general.

► In grade school we did the same thing all the time, and I didn't pay much attention to what I was doing. Now I see a reason for mathematics.

► I used to hate math. The teacher would do some problems and then we would do more like them for homework. It was boring. But I just love this class. I really have to think.

► In my previous years of math, as limited as they are, I have never had the opportunity to think out the answers for myself as I have had this year.

► I think this course is very interesting. In fact I didn't get bored with one thing. My mother and dad found it very interesting too. They would sit down and do some of the interesting things with me. I really enjoyed this course in mathematics.

                              *   *   *

But all student comments do not reflect unqualified approval. How are these for counterpoint?

► I am not a lover of math and this course is no exception.

► I believe that I could become unconfused easily, but it would take time.

► I can't say much about the —————— program because I don't know much about it, but I am sure that the —————— people had the best of intentions.

These last three quotations serve to remind us that "there is no royal road. . . ." The new programs are not courses in mathematics made easy. There will always be some who do not understand, and these pupils may be more acutely aware of their own deficiences in the new programs than they were in the traditional programs. If so, this is probably all to the good.

                              *   *   *

Opinions and attitudes of parents regarding the new programs were also presented. Following is the statement of one teacher:

► Every so often at parents' meetings we try to explain in simple terms what we are trying to do. The vast majority of parents have been most cooperative and understanding. I have been pleased in this respect, and so, I believe, has our administration. But the best ambassadors to the home-front have been the students themselves. From the A student on down to the just-passing student, there is much enthusiasm.

The cooperation of parents in my school district has been excellent. Attendance at open house increased noticeably during the past two years.

As I considered talking to you about parent reaction, I realized I had not received comments from very many of the parents. About three weeks ago we held open house, and in order to get a more comprehensive idea of the parents' viewpoint, I asked them to submit unsigned statements about their children's placement in this course. I emphasized that I wanted their honest expression. With the exception of six or eight, each made a statement to the effect that he was very happy that his child had been given the opportunity to study this mathematics. Most of them said their children found this mathematics more interesting and enjoyable than that which they had studied before. Here are some typical comments:

"My child was never stimulated in previous mathematics classes."
"Wish I were taking it too."
"My son gets along better than my other children did."
"Jealous because I didn't get to study this."
"Seems to have developed a searching quality."
"So different—so interesting—my child never tires of it."
"It has given our youngster a better understanding of mathematics."
"My child loves this mathematics. My only complaint is that it makes me feel so extremely stupid."

Some parents have expressed consternation over their inability to help Johnny with his homework, but I am not too sure that this is bad. Most parents feel gratified that their children are privileged to study these materials.

Here again, as we would expect, we find some parents who are not enchanted by the new mathematics. One such parent wrote, "Take my boy out of this course and put him in a mathematics class." On the other hand there are cases on record where parents moving into a new area have tried to locate in a school district that has one of the improved programs. The evidence presented by our panelists clearly indicates that parents who have been properly informed are generally sympathetic with the school's effort to up-grade the teaching and learning of mathematics through the use of these improved materials of instruction.

*   *   *

The teachers also presented their own views on the results that had been achieved. Here, as we would expect, there are several references to the UICSM program, the only one that has been in operation long enough to obtain information about the students' performances in college.

▶ Referring to the accomplishment of the group as a whole, I have been constantly amazed at the students' ability to comprehend the concepts of the course and at the high level on which they are able to think.

▶ We think the students are getting a better chance to find out what mathematics is all about, to learn that it is a living, growing product of man's mind, not a bag of tricks formulated centuries ago. Because of this we feel we are better able to identify students with real mathematical ability, and this identification is especially significant today. Too often in the past we overlooked some students with real mathematical ability who became bored with the routine and memorization of our courses and did not show up well in evaluations geared to such routines. These students are not apt to be bored with the SMSG texts.

▶ Many of these UICSM students took College Board Examinations and compared favorably with students in the traditional program who took the same examinations. It is our hope that as time goes on and this work progresses, more of the modern mathematics included in this program and in others similar to it will be contained in the College Board Examinations. We have now had four senior groups graduate from this program and most of the students have gained entrance into high-standing schools and have done well in the field of mathematics.

▶ We are presently in the sixth year of teaching the UICSM materials. Our scores on the advanced mathematics achievement tests of the college boards were higher this year than ever before.

▶ What about those students who had four years of the UICSM mathematics who have gone on to college? We have two such groups. These students report that they are being exempted from certain mathematics courses and are, in some instances, being allowed to study honors courses.

*   *   *

The prevailing view among informed teachers is that school mathematics will continue to change. As a consequence the teacher must expect to continue his own education indefinitely. The following statement expresses the consensus on this point:

▶ We, like our students, learn by doing. And regardless of what the future of the mathematics curriculum may be, regardless of what texts we may be using ten years from now, we think that using the SMSG texts, with their different approach, will make us better teachers by broadening our understanding of the mathematics we teach.

4

Implementing a New Mathematics Program in Your School

• W. EUGENE FERGUSON

WHEN WE SPEAK of "the new mathematics program," we do not mean there is only one new program—indeed there are several. We do want to indicate that a good mathematics program for today differs greatly from the program of a few years ago.

I like to speak of *a* new mathematics program for *each* school. Since each school is unique in some respects, it must ultimately develop its own program which will be unique in spite of a great many similarities to programs in other schools.

The problem of introducing a new mathematics program into secondary schools (grades 7 through 12) is very complex. There is no one formula that works for all schools. Following are some characteristic differences that contribute to the difficulty of prescribing a single method of establishing a new mathematics program:

► Schools vary in size from the very small with fewer than 100 students to the very large with several thousand students.

► The percent of college-capable students varies greatly from school to school.

► The capabilities and training of the mathematics teachers vary greatly. Some teachers have had little or no college mathematics while others have had 60 or more credit hours.

► Community attitudes toward mathematics programs vary. Some communities display complete apathy and unwillingness to disturb the *status quo*; others show enthusiasm for change, but meet resistance from faculty members untrained in the newer approaches to mathematics.

Dr. Ferguson is head of the Mathematics Department at Newton High School, Newtonville, Massachusetts.

Since implementing a new mathematics program is an individual problem that is unique for each school, I cannot tell you specifically how to proceed in your school. I can and shall, however, describe techniques of implementation that have been found useful in various school systems. It will be your job to select those ideas you feel are appropriate and reformulate some of them into workable patterns for your particular situation. I shall present certain ideas that I consider essential, and I shall make a strong case for them. At the same time I fully realize that it may be necessary for you to vary the ideas or techniques slightly in applying them.

STEPS IN IMPLEMENTATION

Following are eight steps I consider basic to the implementation process. I shall discuss each of them, describing and evaluating the techniques involved. There is, necessarily, some overlapping of techniques among the steps, as you will see in the discussion.

1. Recognition by school authorities of the need for a new mathematics program.
2. Adequate preparation of teachers in the mathematics now being taught for the first time in secondary schools.
3. Selection of a new program.
4. Selection of students for the program.
5. Informing parents about the new program.
6. Informing other members of the school system about the new program and its implications for the mathematics program K-12.
7. Continuation of teacher preparation for carrying the new program to higher and lower grades.
8. Provision for adequate time and compensation to carry on the new program year after year.

Those of us who have implemented new programs in mathematics, even as recently as three years ago, recognize that the implementation job has changed. It changes even from year to year because of the tremendous growth of the new programs in mathematics and the general availability of teaching materials for them.

1. RECOGNIZING THE NEED

The first of the eight steps is really a prerequisite of change, since the need must be recognized by school authorities before any change can be made. School authorities include mathematics teachers and supervisors, superintendents, principals and their assistants in charge of curriculum development, and the school committees or school boards—in fact, any personnel responsible in any way for the school mathematics curriculum. The question to be answered is this: *How do schools develop a recognition of the need for a new program?*

Many teachers have become interested in new mathematics programs as a result of reading reports in *The Mathematics Teacher* and *The Arithmetic Teacher*, the professional journals of the National Council of Teachers of Mathematics. Teachers have learned about the new programs and new texts at mathematics institutes sponsored by the National Science Foundation; they often return to their own schools and inspire colleagues to compare the traditional mathematics program with one of the newer ones.

Principals and superintendents in some schools have urged teachers to attend summer institutes or academic-year institutes sponsored by the National Science Foundation. Some administrators have arranged payment of expenses for teachers attending summer school.

It is clear that teachers recognize the need for change as soon as they learn about the newer mathematics that is being taught successfully in secondary schools.

Some teachers, however, have said that they were ready to start a new program in mathematics, but they could not get the administration to cooperate. Money to help implement the program was not available. Implementing a new mathematics program is really a cooperative venture for both the mathematics teachers and the administration. Teachers cannot possibly do it alone. They need the sympathetic encouragement and active help of the administration.

Principals have learned of the new mathematics programs from the 190-page report on "New Developments in Secondary School Mathematics," in the May 1959 issue of the *Bulletin* of the National Association of Secondary School Principals. A reprint of this report may be obtained from the National Council of Teachers of Mathematics.

The report of the Secondary School Curriculum Committee of the National Council of Teachers of Mathematics was published in the May 1959 issue of *The Mathematics Teacher*. It presents the findings of eleven subcommittees and gives directions for strengthening and improving mathematics education in secondary schools. This is also available as a reprint.

A quick survey of new programs in mathematics that have gained some measure of national recognition is given in *Studies in Mathematics Education—A Brief Survey of Improvement Programs for School Mathematics*, published by Scott, Foresman & Company.

2. ADEQUATE PREPARATION OF TEACHERS

The adequate preparation of teachers in the mathematics now being taught for the first time in secondary schools is a natural next step after recognition of the need for a new mathematics program. In general, when school authorities are convinced a new program is needed, they realize, at the same time, that their teachers are inadequately prepared. So how have school systems prepared their teachers for new programs? In some cases teachers have attended summer institutes where they studied basic mathematics; in addition they participated in seminars on one of the new programs—UICSM, SMSG, or UMMaP, for example—or they studied the Appendices of the Report of the Commission on Mathematics of the College Entrance Examination Board. Some summer institutes have offered demonstration classes where teachers could observe the new materials being taught to secondary school students. The discovery method of teaching the UICSM materials has been used in such demonstration classes.

Many schools have engaged mathematicians interested in the new secondary school programs; these mathematicians give the teachers in-service mathematics courses in the new approaches recommended by the various groups developing new curricula. Where it is not feasible for a single school system to have these services, several school systems may work together in offering such in-service mathematics courses to their teachers. If the head of the mathematics department, or a member of the department, is adequately prepared, he may teach the in-service courses.

Some colleges offer for credit a curriculum and methods course in mathematics which serves many school systems in their areas. The new mathematics content makes up the major part of such courses, but the discovery method of teaching also gets some attention. It is clear that there are two aspects to consider in training teachers to handle the new programs: (a) teaching the new mathematics content and the techniques for teaching it, and (b) teaching the new approaches to the familiar mathematics content. For many teachers the second aspect is the harder.

Schools initiating new programs would be wise to take a cue from SMSG and have adequate professional assistance available for the teachers as they progress through a new course for the first time. Some departments have found it helpful to have a mathematician available as consultant to answer questions in a session with the teachers once every two or three weeks. When this is not feasible, a high school teacher adequately educated in the particular subject may suffice. But competent help from some source must be available to teachers at least their first time through a new course. In general the best help comes from a supervisor who knows the mathematics and has taught the new material so that he is familiar with reactions to it.

In schools that do not have a qualified mathematician available to direct the study, groups of teachers have taken the SMSG and/or UICSM material and have worked it out together using the teachers' commentary and the combined knowledge of the group. This procedure has merit for school systems that are somewhat isolated from other opportunities for teacher education. Such groups need leaders, and teachers who have attended summer institutes may be good leaders. Tact and diplomacy are required, of course, but the net result in improving the mathematics program is worth the effort.

It is the experience of many of us who have been working with the new materials for the past four years that as an entire staff becomes well trained in a new program, the so-called traditional classes in that school have taken on a new look also. This, of course, is precisely what we want, and in time the new programs will take over completely. The change will be faster than most of us ever dared dream possible.

3. SELECTING THE PROGRAM

The third step in implementation, after the teachers have learned some of the newer approaches to mathematics, is the selection of a new program. It is important that teachers be somewhat acquainted with the various new mathematics programs *before* a specific program is selected. We realize that it is possible for a strong department head to decide to use the UICSM, or SMSG, or other program, or a combination of two or more, and then proceed to get his staff adequately prepared. However, it its doubtful that an intelligent choice can be made unless someone involved in the decision is well acquainted with the content of the various programs and the teaching techniques and materials available.

My attention has been called to the fact that some administrators and school boards have decided to institute new mathematics programs in their schools in September, but they had not yet decided by July who would do the teaching! Of course mathematics teachers in these schools were worried, and they had reason to be. No teacher should be asked to take on a new program without adequate advance provision for the necessary education. On the other hand, some teachers have had ample time and warning to become prepared to teach a new program in mathematics, but have not done anything about it. Some teachers face real problems in becoming prepared, and I shall have more to say about this with step 7.

No matter who chooses the new program, adequate provision must be made in advance to have teachers properly educated and qualified to see it through to completion in grade 12. This does not mean that the selection must be one of the existing programs all the way; it does mean that the new program must have some sort of continuity through grade 12. At no time should the teachers feel they have been left "high and dry" with no logical next step. Many teachers feel that at least in the beginning they should choose one program and stay with it. This is not absolutely necessary if the teachers involved understand how to put two or more programs together to make one good program. However, this is not an easy task.

All teachers are urged to put as much as possible of the new mathematics content into their secondary school classes, even without changing the textbooks. It is obvious that all textbooks cannot be changed immediately, but the courses can be improved immediately if teachers will study, learn, and teach the content of the new programs even though it is not in their textbooks. This is obviously more difficult than adopting one of the new programs, and less effective.

There are three points I should like to stress in connection with the selection of a new program:

► Whoever is to make the decision should study the various programs and decide which one or combination of two or more is best suited for his school staff and student body.

▶ The teachers must be properly prepared to start the program. Further education of teachers to continue the program through grade 12 must be made available. Teacher preparation must keep ahead of the new program as it progresses through grade 12.

▶ Adequate professional help must be available to assist the teachers as they progress through the new courses for the first time.

4. Selecting the Students

The fourth step is the selection of students for the new program. In the UICSM program it has been found that teachers do a better job and feel more comfortable the first time through the course with selected homogeneous groups of better than average ability. Many new programs are for college-capable students, and the better ones of this group probably represent the top 25 percent of the student body. After the teacher has gone through the course once, he can more comfortably teach the material to any group of college-capable students. In large school systems honor sections should move much faster and deeper into the new material than other groups. Where homogeneous grouping is impossible, teachers are still introducing these new materials and doing it successfully.

New programs will cost more money because in many schools classes may be small in order to get top quality students to start the program. In some cases a new teacher must be added to keep from making the class size in the traditional courses too large.

It is far too early to make predictions about the new programs, but I shall tell you the experience of my high school. In the school year 1959-60 we had two well-trained teachers presenting SMSG geometry to 130 sophomores (4 classes). The students were unselected except for the fact that they were in the college preparatory curriculum. While our measuring device was probably crude, it is significant that when these students were compared with those in the traditional geometry course, the better students in the new program did better, the poorer students did poorer.

One important outcome of our experience is that the teachers hope they will never have to go back to the traditional geometry textbook. They believe that as they become more experienced with the new programs they will be able to do a better job teaching the less able students. Therefore we urge that schools start new programs with the better homogeneous groups. This obviously means that each school will have so-called traditional classes as well as classes using the new program. It would be an exceptional school indeed that had all of its mathematics staff ready to teach a new program in all classes from the very beginning. But if your school, small or large, has its total staff ready to teach a new program, you should make haste to introduce it in *all* college preparatory mathematics classes. For transfer students it is sometimes helpful to have a so-called traditional course, but this should not be a controlling factor. Materials for the average and for the slow child will become available as we learn how to get these new materials across to students of more limited capability.

A combination of parts of the UICSM first course and parts of the SMSG 7th and 8th grade courses—in the hands of an experienced teacher of the new programs—shows promise of being an exciting and interesting general mathematics course for grade 10.

Judging from what the students in new programs have accomplished so far, it is clear to many teachers that we have underestimated the mathematical power of our students, particularly in grades 4 through 9. Selecting students for the new programs worries some teachers who may say, "I don't have enough students who can master this material to make even one class; it is too difficult for them." Experience with many excellent traditional mathematics teachers indicates that teachers have more difficulty changing to a new program than students do.

The reason is apparent, but it is a point that even teachers have difficulty understanding. It is not easy for us as teachers to change our way of looking at mathematics. Over a period of years we have built up certain reactions and language patterns when confronted with a mathematical problem. For many of these problems the new programs have changed the approach and language and in many cases the symbolism also. Since the student has not seen this material before, he sees nothing strange about it at all; teachers, however, are forced to unlearn or forget the old approach and learn the new one. This is difficult, but it leads to a beautiful argument for the new programs: they are written in such a way that the student does not have to unlearn anything when he gets into an up-to-date college mathematics course. The new programs fit into the language of advanced mathematics, since they present the subject as the mathematician of today sees it and talks about it.

5. Informing the Parents

The fifth step in the process of implementation is informing parents about the new program. Many parents become uneasy when they can't do Johnny's homework; the transition will be much smoother if parents are informed about the aims of the new programs. The UICSM has been working on a new program in mathematics since 1952, and I shall draw upon their experience. PTA meetings have been scheduled to discuss the UICSM program. A seminar to teach the parents the new approach was organized by a teacher in one school at the request of interested parents.

In my own school system each junior high school held a yearly open meeting the first two or three years with parents of those students invited to study the UICSM materials. We have not found it necessary to discuss the SMSG high school program in a public meeting, since many of the parents involved had attended a meeting on the junior high school UICSM program. Once a new program is introduced to the parents, it is doubtful that it will be necessary to meet with them every year. When the program dips further down to include lower grade-levels, the open meetings should be held for parents of those students. In other words, parents should be informed about the new methods of teaching mathematics at the time their children enter one of the new programs.

While there have been many popular articles written about the new mathematics programs, a discussion of the particular new program with parents will make them more sympathetic and will give them an understanding of the school's position if the new courses become difficult for some of the students. Although the teachers believe the new programs are better, some students still have trouble with the material. If parents have not been properly prepared, they may blame the program for their child's difficulty. For example, the student with an excellent capacity for rote memory may find that "thinking out" for himself some of the newer concepts in mathematics requires more mental effort than he is willing to expend, and as a result his grades drop. Our belief is that the rote memory is short-lived, and in the end will net very little real mathematical learning that will be useful years hence. But we must communicate this belief to the parents.

Another way of informing parents about a new mathematics program is to send home with the student a one- or two-page report on the program, giving its aims and the school's hopes for its success. We must have specific reasons for believing that the new program is better, otherwise why bother to change? Many parents want to know the precise reasons for the change. In addition, it is helpful for teachers to verbalize their own feelings and state precisely why they prefer the new program.

Parents will be impressed by the fact that students in the new programs are holding their own on traditional tests; this means they have mastered the traditional material. In addition, they have absorbed new material and show an enthusiasm for mathematics that many of them did not have before. Another important point that must not be overlooked is the fact that the Educational Testing Service is preparing new Cooperative Achievement Tests to cover the material in the new programs. I have reviewed some of these tests, and I am quite sure that my students who are still studying mathematics from the traditional books will not be very successful with them. My students who are studying mathematics using one of the new programs will be qualified to handle the tests quite well. The College Board tests are also changing.

6. Informing Others in the School System

The sixth step is to inform other members of the school system about the new program and its implications for the mathematics curriculum, kindergarten through grade 12. It is important that other departments in the school system be aware of the new mathematics program; such information will save them embarrassment when they are asked about it.

Another aspect of this step is even more important. Each school system must establish communication lines among all mathematics teachers, kindergarten through grade 12, and all other people responsible for the mathematics curriculum, so that they can study the implications of the new program for all grades. Consider the old criticism of mathematics instruction. Senior high school teachers blame junior high school teachers and junior high school teachers blame elementary school teachers for passing inadequately prepared students to the next level. To eliminate such criticisms, we must have coordinated K through 12 programs in which each student is passed to the next higher course that most nearly meets his needs.

Since the SMSG program is producing materials of instruction for grades 4 through 12, it is clear that coordination is necessary. If a child starting the SMSG program in grade 7 is to gain maximum benefit from his experience, his training in grades 1 through 6 should be quite different from what it is today in most schools.

The UICSM program may be started in grade 8 with selected children, or in grade 7 with exceptionally bright children. Here also change is desirable in activities for grades 1 through 6 as well as grades 9 through 12. In a practical sense the junior high school teacher (grades 7, 8, and 9) should know the high school program (grades 10, 11, and 12); and the elementary teacher (grades 1 through 6) should know at least the 7th, 8th, and 9th grade programs. For most schools, therefore, in-service education courses should be set up to instruct teachers in the new mathematics they are supposed to teach and to show how it fits in with preceding and succeeding levels. Junior high school teachers should be invited to—and expected to attend—in-service education courses in the high school subjects after they master the mathematics content for grades 7 through 9. High school teachers should certainly know the course content and teaching methods used in grades 7, 8, and 9.

7. Continuing Teacher Preparation

Step 7, continuation of teacher preparation for carrying the new program to higher and lower grades, has many aspects that need to be explored. We have said that once a new program is started in a particular grade, provision should be made to continue through grade 12. While it is not absolutely necessary, any departure from this plan should be carefully thought out.

Experience has shown that school systems large enough should have at least two teachers in each building teaching the same new course. To be a "lone wolf" in this sort of project is difficult, because one needs to be able to talk over the problems that arise. In order to develop a precise language in mathematics one needs to practice it on fellow teachers who can point out ambiguous and imprecise statements. This precise language cannot be expected of the student until he has heard his teacher use it for a considerable period of time. Old habits and language are difficult to change; those who are used to the traditional language of mathematics need time to learn the new symbolism and make it part of them.

It will now be profitable for us to expand the discussion begun under Step 2, touching upon the financial aspects of the education program necessary for teachers.

All groups that have been developing new courses for secondary school mathematics have recognized the need for the re-education of teachers in the new content and in new approaches to the old, familiar content. The UICSM project has offered summer conferences for teachers of their courses. The content of the SMSG and the UICSM programs and the recommendations of the Commission on Mathematics are being taught and discussed in many summer institutes sponsored by the National Science Foundation. More and more teachers colleges and universities include the new materials in their curriculum and methods courses in mathematics. It is inevitable, however, that in the beginning, opportunities for getting proper education in the new courses will be somewhat limited.

Since a teacher's salary is not usually adequate to support his family without summer employment, the school system must make some sort of payment so that the teacher will be financially able to attend summer school for special education in the new programs. This is a new function, but a necessary one, for many school systems if they expect to institute new mathematics programs in the near future. Industry has recognized its responsibility for the special education of its personnel. It has pointed the way, and many school systems are following. The Federal Government through the National Science Foundation has recognized the necessity of re-educating teachers and is putting millions of dollars into the various institute programs at colleges and universities. These pay all expenses plus a stipend to offset the loss of income while teachers attend the institutes.

Some schools have paid the expenses of teachers studying the UICSM program at the University of Illinois. Others have given the teachers a flat sum, $500 or a month's salary, and the teachers have paid their own expenses. The essential point here is recognition by the school system of its responsibility to pay or at least help to pay for the re-education of its staff.

Some schools have set up in-service education courses in mathematics taught by a member of their own staff or a mathematician from a nearby college. These courses prepare teachers to handle the next course in the sequence of a new program. Some schools have reduced the teaching load from 5 to 4 classes for those teaching a new program to give them time for preparation.

In many schools where the services of a college mathematician are not available a member of the staff who has attended an academic year institute or summer institute teaches the in-service courses. Some remuneration and some reduction in teaching load should be made for a teacher directing these courses. In some schools the non-professional, non-teaching load has been reduced to give teachers time to do a good job with their present teaching assignment and also give them time to prepare for the new courses the following year.

During the year of experimentation with the preliminary edition of SMSG materials a mathematician serves as consultant to a group of eight to ten teachers who are teaching the same course. Reports from the teachers indicate that this type of professional help gives them the assurance and confidence they need to do a superb job in teaching the new material. Teachers' questions about the mathematics content and the way it fits into the total mathematics picture can be answered quickly and effectively.

All teachers should take advantage of the courses in contemporary mathematics to be offered again by Continental Classroom in 1961-62 at 6:00 a.m. in all time zones on NBC-TV. During the first semester, starting on September 25, Professor John L. Kelley of the University of California at Berkeley lectures three days a week on Modern Algebra. The other two days Professor Kelley and Dr. Julius H. Hlavaty answer questions, solve problems and exercises, and relate the mathematics in the lectures to the mathematics in the new programs in high school. Students as well as teachers are viewing this course. A once-a-week seminar with interested students and mathematics teachers, using the textbook written by Professor Kelley to supplement these lectures, would prove very rewarding. The second semester course is on Probability and Statistics, taught by Professor Frederick Mosteller of Harvard University, with Professor Paul Clifford of Montclair Teachers College relating the material to the high school program.

Administrators may find it interesting to view this program and to surprise the mathematics teachers by asking appropriate questions. Moreover, this might bring about improved communication between administrators and the mathematics department. The teachers certainly need sympathetic interest and encouragement while they are in the midst of the change and development of the new curriculum.

To support a new program each school system must acquire an adequate library of reference material for students and teachers. This may be obtained with the help of National Defense Education Act funds. There is much new material that can be read independently by students, and it is necessary that they learn how to use the library in the study of mathematics. This type of training is very important in developing the ability of students to do independent work. The library is also very helpful to teachers, particularly while they are studying the new programs. If money is short for buying the necessary new books and materials, why not try to get industries in the school district to assist in supplying books?

When a new program is introduced at any level from grade 7 through 12, it becomes clear that work in the preceding grade level must be changed to prepare students properly for the new material. Whatever the grade level at which the new program starts, changes must be made in the earlier grades, and the program should be continued through grade 12. Some people say that if this is the case, it would be logical to start a new program in kindergarten and develop it year after year. I agree that we should start now with the kindergarten, but we must also start now at every grade level. The present senior class should not be graduated without being exposed to some of the new content and new approaches. This obviously creates some confusion and turmoil, but it is the price we have to pay for the speedy change that is now so essential. If more of the curricular changes that were recommended at various times from 1900 to 1950 had been gradually incorporated during those years, we would not now be pressing for speedy change.

8. Time and Compensation for Work on New Programs

The eighth and final step, provision for adequate time and compensation for carrying on a new program year after year, has been discussed somewhat in the previous steps. It must be made clear to the administration and the school board that a new program in mathematics will cost more for books and materials, and this increase must be budgeted so that money will be available.

Participating teachers need adequate time for study and preparation. The housekeeping and extra-curricular duties they must perform should be kept to a minimum. Some schools have eliminated study hall duty from the schedules of teachers in the new programs; this is an excellent move. More clerical help should be made available to relieve the teachers. In fact, teachers who spend time doing clerical work are high-priced clerks, and many are less efficient at this work than good secretaries.

Proper compensation must be provided. In the past, schools have paid teachers to write new curricula during the summer. Many times these teachers merely reshuffled the old, traditional content; this did not make a more inspiring course.

I know of a school system that paid $5.00 per hour, four hours a day ($100 a week) for six weeks to teachers who went to school during the summer to study the new courses they were to teach in the fall. Then on two Saturdays a month during the school year, for four hours at $5.00 per hour, these teachers met with a consultant in mathematics to discuss questions that occurred to them and to their students that needed further clarification. This is an excellent procedure. It helps keep teachers in a system because of the extra pay they receive during the summer while they are working to improve their teaching.

Industry sends employees to school, paying their regular salaries as well as tuition fees and expenses; this same idea could very well be copied by school systems that want their mathematics personnel qualified to handle new programs. Many school systems are setting up continuing in-service education programs to insure that their mathematics staffs are adequately trained at all times.

*   *   *

It is obvious, I am sure, that the implementation of a new mathematics program does not occur in eight nice, neat, orderly steps. Many of the ideas presented occur simultaneously. Each school has its own implementation problems; the best we can hope to do is to indicate how some school systems have solved theirs. You have to determine which methods will work for you.

ADVANCED PLACEMENT PROGRAM

The new programs I have concerned myself with in this paper do not include the Advanced Placement Program—calculus and analytic geometry in the senior year of high school—which is being adopted by more and more schools. The results of the advanced placement test in May 1960 indicate that many students who took the exam were unprepared. I shall not attempt to guess why the students were unprepared; instead I shall outline what is considered a good way to implement a bona fide college calculus and analytic geometry course in the senior year of high school.

Before a high school mathematics department offers a full year calculus and analytic geometry course, certain conditions *must* be met by the school, the teachers, and the students.

The school must have a curriculum offering that allows the student to complete the mathematics prerequisites for calculus and analytic geometry by the end of the junior year. In some schools this means elementary algebra in grade 8, intermediate algebra in grade 9, plane and solid geometry in grade 10, college algebra, trigonometry and some coordinate geometry in grade 11. It is possible for very bright youngsters to take elementary algebra in grade 9, then do two years work (geometry and intermediate algebra) in grade 10, but I do not recommend this procedure. We have done this for seven years in my own school, but we are getting away from it by starting the UICSM program in grade 8. We also find that some students can do a whole year's work in six weeks of summer school if their desire for calculus in the senior year is strong enough.

There must be at least one teacher on the staff who can give a bona fide calculus course on the college level as outlined in the Advanced Placement Program of the College Entrance Examination Board. Many teachers have gone back to school to take calculus courses again, and they are now doing an excellent job of teaching calculus to high school seniors.

The student must be mathematically prepared for the course and must be willing to spend eight to ten hours a week on homework. He must be adequately motivated for taking the calculus.

If the school, the teacher, and the student meet these conditions for an Advanced Placement Program, the student will receive adequate preparation for the advanced placement examination.

WHY MAKE ANY CHANGE?

Administrators are asking, "What evidence do you have that the new mathematics programs are better than the old ones? We produced some topnotch mathematicians with the old programs." However, some of us who have taught the traditional mathematics program feel it is a miracle that some of our students became mathematicians considering the way we taught them.

Here is the evidence we have to date that the new programs are an improvement: Teachers are very enthusiastic about the new mathematics programs and the new teaching techniques; students show more interest and enthusiasm for mathematics than ever before; almost all (if not all) teachers in the new programs—UICSM, SMSG, UMMaP, etc.,—do not want to return to teaching the traditional texts. The mathematics in the new programs is not easier, it is not watered down; on the contrary, it is more interesting and challenging to students and teachers alike. We believe that on traditional tests, students taking the new programs have performed approximately as well as the students in traditional courses. If this is the case, the students taking the new programs have the same mathematical knowledge as the students taught in the traditional manner, plus many new ideas and topics. On power tests, such as the Advanced Mathematics Examination of the College Entrance Examination Board and the Contest Examination of the Mathematical Association of America, the results are different. In schools that have used the UICSM Program for three or more years, the students in the new program have done significantly better than students of comparable ability who have had only the traditional courses.

If my students taking the new programs can hold their own with traditionally taught students on the traditional tests in the early stages, I am satisfied. It will take time to obtain more proof of the superiority of the new programs. One teacher asked me to tell administrators and teachers that instead of demanding black and white proof of the superiority of new programs at this time, they must have faith in the experiences of other schools that have used the materials and have found them very successful. I am stubborn enough to say that if my colleagues can be successful with this new material, then so can I. I hope more teachers and administrators will take this attitude and will not be afraid to try the new material.

There is one more bit of compelling evidence: Many distinguished mathematicians have helped produce these new mathematics programs and they have certified the new content as correct and significant mathematics for our times.

IS MATHEMATICS EASY TO TEACH?

Administrators must not be afraid to initiate a new program in mathematics *if* the teachers are adequately prepared and willing to teach it.

In the past some administrators thought that mathematics was so easy to teach—the same, year after year—that anybody could teach it. Therefore, they assigned mathematics classes to some teachers who were not mathematically qualified. Administrators must give up the idea that mathematics is easy to teach. The day is gone when the administrator can assign just anyone on his staff to teach mathematics and come up with an acceptable program. Mathematics must not be taught today with the same content and techniques that have been commonly used in the past.

TIMETABLE FOR CHANGE

I have hinted at the problem of timing in the orderly process of implementing a new program in your school. Let us be a little more specific. Suppose I wish to start teaching a new program in the fall of 1962. Then no later than the fall of 1961, my teachers and I must do an intensive study of the materials available and decide which program offers the sequential courses through grade 12 that I want. By January 15, 1962, we must make our decision, assign the teachers, and immediately start an in-service training course using the actual materials to be taught to the students. This in-service training course should be attended by all teachers whether or not they will be teaching in the program in 1962-63.

If the school system is large enough, a committee should review the various offerings of the many National Science Foundation summer institutes and encourage teachers to apply to those institutes whose offerings will best prepare them to teach the program adopted for their schools.

During 1962-63 in-service training for the next course in the sequence must be offered to and attended by all teachers. Also during 1962-63 other teachers who are qualified should start in the program—preferably teaching the beginning course in the sequence and then following on through the total program, or as far as they are qualified to go. An ideal setup for the summer would be to have a group of teachers attend the same institute so that they will develop the feeling of the team approach as soon as possible.

The school should pay the stipend and expenses for any teachers above the age limit for the particular institute chosen.

A modest start is all that is required. The best way to sell a new program to teachers and parents is to show it working in at least one class in your school. With all teachers studying the program in the in-service course, the traditional courses will soon take on a new look.

Mathematics teachers must devote a lot of time and work to keeping up with the new programs, content, and teaching techniques during the next few years, and the schools must find a way to compensate them for this extra time. Teaching techniques must not be overlooked, and no matter which program is used, I urge you to consider the UICSM Teacher Training Films. Information concerning these films may be obtained from Professor Max Beberman at the University of Illinois.

I hope I have created in you a sense of the urgency facing us as a nation for the implementation of new mathematics programs in our schools. The job will not be done overnight. Diligent effort is required or we shall be left behind. It is clear that playing a waiting game until one single program emerges as *the* mathematics program is playing a losing game—there never will be *one* mathematics program.

Since many school systems, large and small, have successfully implemented new programs in mathematics, we are confident that with the cooperation and combined efforts of both administrators and teachers, any school system can have a new program in mathematics.

5

Questions and Answers

A GREAT DEAL of interest and enthusiasm was generated by the speeches, the panel discussions, and the group meetings at each of the Regional Orientation Conferences. This was clearly indicated by the large number and thoughtful quality of questions submitted in writing by the conferees. The replies were given at question and answer sessions by Frank B. Allen, Kenneth E. Brown, W. Eugene Ferguson, and G. Baley Price, who made up the Consultant Panel.

At the conclusion of the conferences these questions and answers were turned over to the Director. There were several hundred, but the task of summarizing was simplified because certain questions were asked, although in different form, at each of the conferences and because well-defined classifications were discernible. We have made use of these classifications to present some of the questions that were raised at every one of the eight conferences.

We feel that the pattern of questions is significant as an illustration of the thinking of superintendents, principals, supervisors, curriculum directors, and department chairmen. These school officials will determine the extent to which new mathematics programs will be used in the classrooms.

To increase the usefulness of this section, we have brought the answers up to date where changes have occurred since the conferences. Such changes relate to titles, contents, publishers, prices, and manner of distribution of books and units published, as well as any change in the location or personnel for the new programs.

We hope that the questions and answers below will prove helpful.

ADMINISTRATIVE PROBLEMS

AVAILABILITY OF MATERIALS

To what extent and on what terms are the materials produced by the new programs actually available for classroom use?

In answering this question we shall consider the programs individually.

University of Illinois Committee on School Mathematics

The UICSM project has developed teaching units for grades 9-12 for the college-capable student. (In many schools these materials are started in the 8th grade.) Units in use or in preparation are:

Unit	Descriptive Title
1	The arithmetic of the real numbers
2	Generalizations and algebraic manipulation
3	Equations and inequations
4	Ordered pairs and graphs
5	Relations and functions
6	Geometry
7	Mathematical induction
8	Sequences
9	Exponential and logarithmic functions
10	Circular functions and trigonometry
11	Polynomial functions and complex numbers

Units 1 through 8 are now available for general use in schools. Unit 9 will be published in January 1962, and Units 10 and 11 in August 1962. Copies of the paperbound students' edition and of the looseleaf teachers' edition, which includes a copy of the students' edition, are available from the University of Illinois Press (Urbana, Illinois). Please specify the edition desired and use the following descriptions when ordering:

UICSM Units 1-4 of *High School Mathematics*
    Student edition   708 p. $3.00
    Teacher edition 1468 p. $6.00

UICSM Unit 5 of *High School Mathematics*
    Student edition   300 p. $1.50
    Teacher edition   620 p. $3.00

UICSM Unit 6 of *High School Mathematics*
    Student edition   458 p. $2.00
    Teacher edition   964 p. $4.00

UICSM Unit 7 of *High School Mathematics*
    Student edition   166 p. $1.25
    Teacher edition   427 p. $2.75

UICSM Unit 8 of *High School Mathematics*
    Student edition   264 p. $1.75
    Teacher edition   700 p.   (est.) $4.00

Units 1 through 4 are available individually in the students' edition at $1.00 per unit. They are not available individually in the teachers' edition.

Although these units and related teachers' editions are now available commercially, the UICSM project does not recommend their unrestricted classroom use. It has been found that probability of success with Units 1 through 6 is closely allied with adequate teacher preparation—a concentrated institute or seminar course in which teachers study and discuss the content of the units and see live or filmed demonstrations of children studying the same material. The UICSM Project extends good will and good wishes to the many teachers who are introducing these materials without specific preparation, but does not assume responsibility for such use.

School Mathematics Study Group

Yale University Press has taken over a major portion of the printing and distributing operations for the School Mathematics Study Group. Students' texts and teachers' commentaries for junior and senior high school mathematics are now available only through Yale University Press, and orders for these books will no longer be handled by the SMSG office. The address for ordering texts and teachers' commentaries is Yale University Press, School Mathematics Study Group, 92A Yale Station, New Haven, Connecticut.

The SMSG issued most of the texts in three parts. A different format has been chosen for the volumes by Yale University Press. Each text and each commentary for grades 7 through 11 is now being issued in two parts and sold as a set. There are two separate books for the 12th grade, and a teachers' commentary for each of them. The size of the books has been reduced from the original 8½ x 11 inches to 7 x 10 inches.

Following is a list of SMSG publications now available only through Yale University Press:

Mathematics for Junior High School
Grades 7 and 8

Grade	Title	Price
7	Volume 1, Parts I and II	$3.00
	Teachers' Commentary, Parts I and II	3.00
8	Volume 2, Parts I and II	3.00
	Teachers' Commentary, Parts I and II	3.00

Mathematics for High School
Grades 9 through 12

Grade	Title	Price
9	First Course in Algebra, Parts I and II	$3.00
	Teachers' Commentary, Parts I and II	3.00
10	Geometry, Parts I and II	3.00
	Teachers' Commentary, Parts I and II	3.00
11	Intermediate Mathematics, Parts I and II	3.00
	Teachers' Commentary, Parts I and II	3.00
12	Elementary Functions	2.00
	Teachers' Commentary	2.00
12	Introduction to Matrix Algebra	2.00
	Teachers' Commentary	2.00

The Yale University Press offers discounts of 40 percent to accredited schools and 10 percent to accredited libraries.

Other SMSG publications will continue to be distributed by the School

Mathematics Study Group. These include the following series: Studies in Mathematics, Supplementary Units, Conference Reports, Mathematics for the Elementary School, and the New Mathematics Library. Inquiries about and orders for these publications should be addressed to the School Mathematics Study Group, Box 2029 Yale Station, New Haven, Connecticut.

It should be kept in mind that most secondary school teachers, through no fault of their own, did not receive undergraduate training in the mathematics required for the use of these texts. When teaching with these texts for the first time, therefore, most teachers need some help in the form of additional mathematics training. Experience in the SMSG Experimental Centers suggests that an in-service training program taught by a subject matter specialist either before or during the first year's use of the texts will adequately deal with this problem. We also learn from the SMSG experience that the second time through a course the teacher needs very little in-service assistance and extra time for preparation; in many cases the need for such assistance and extra time is entirely eliminated. A detailed discussion of SMSG's experience with in-service assistance to teachers may be found in the SMSG *Newsletter* No. 5.

Ball State Teachers College Experimental Program

Three textbooks in the Ball State Series have been published by the Addison-Wesley Publishing Company, Reading, Massachusetts. A teachers' manual is available for each of the books. The titles and prices are as follows:

Introduction to Mathematics	
Student Text	$4.00
Teachers' Manual	2.68
Algebra I	
Student Text	5.08
Teachers' Manual	2.68
Geometry	
Student Text	5.08
Teachers' Manual	2.68

University of Maryland Mathematics Project

Mathematics for the Junior High School, First and Second Books, will be available for use in classes during 1961-62. Each text has been revised after extensive classroom use. The prices are as follows:

	Paper Cover	Hard Cover
Mathematics for the Junior High School, First Book		
Student Text	$2.25	$3.25
Teachers' Manual	2.00	
Mathematics for the Junior High School, Second Book		
Student Text	2.25	3.25
Teachers' Manual	2.00	

A limited number of the paper-cover student texts remains. When this supply is exhausted, only hard-cover copies will be available. The teachers' manuals are bound only in paper covers.

The sale of classroom sets of UMMaP texts will be approved only if the teacher has the necessary background and if local consultant service is available. However, teachers may purchase individual copies for their own use.

Boston College Mathematics Series

Course 1 of *Sets, Operations, and Patterns* is now available in the students' edition and teachers' manual. It is recommended for use starting in grade 7 and continuing through part of grade 8. Course 2, scheduled for publication in June 1962, is planned for grades 8 and 9, and there will be additional courses carrying the program through Grade 12. The prices for Course 1 are as follows:

Students' Edition (paperbound, approx. 850 p.) $5.00
Teachers' Manual 1.00

The teachers' manual is sent free with orders of 20 or more copies of the students' edition.

STATE ADOPTIONS

Some states adopt approved lists of texts from which schools must choose. How can we have added to our state's approved lists those texts that present the new mathematics programs?

Commenting on the "how" enters the field of administrative procedure where administrators are obviously better informed than educators. Moreover, it may not be necessary to name these new texts on state adoption lists in order to make them available to the schools on an interim basis. Schools should apply to their State Department of Public Instruction for permission to use the new materials on an experimental basis. In many cases the requests will be granted. During the period of transition, steps should be taken to liberalize or suspend any state or local regulation that acts as a barrier to the immediate use of the improved texts. A state adoption list may be such a barrier. Another is the "five-year rule" which requires that a text be retained for at least five years after the date of its initial adoption.

Some schools may find it possible to cover the cost of providing the improved texts by increasing the amount of money appropriated for the purchase of supplementary materials of instruction.

School administrators are in a position to deal effectively with practical difficulties such as these, and they will do so once they are convinced that the new mathematics programs must be readily accessible to their schools.

COMMERCIAL TEXTS

Is it expected that commercial publishers will provide texts based on the improved materials?

Yes. A major objective of the new programs is to bring about a general improvement in mathematics textbooks. For this reason, commercial publishers have a vital role in the upgrading of school mathematics. They should study the improved materials and make cloth-bound, typographically attractive, carefully edited versions available as soon as possible.

Mathematicians and teachers working together *can* produce texts that are both teachable and mathematically sound. It is hoped that commercial publishers will be influenced by this pattern of production as well as by the improved texts resulting from it.

There is evidence that textbook publishers are aware of their obligations in this matter and that they are preparing to capitalize on their opportunities to produce improved texts. Part of the Ball State program is already commercially available. The same is true of the UICSM program where the first eight units are now commercially available and three more will be commercially available in 1962. The SMSG has had so many inquiries from publishers that the following statement of policy on the use of SMSG materials has been authorized by the Advisory Committee: [1]

SMSG has prepared a series of sample texts designed to illustrate, in a concrete fashion, the kind of curriculum which the members of SMSG believe should be taught in the schools of this country. It is not intended that the SMSG texts be considered as the only suitable ones for such a curriculum. Indeed a variety of texts of the same general nature is not only possible but also highly desirable. It is expected that these will become available through the usual commercial channels in the near future.

A major purpose of an SMSG text is to serve as a model and as a source of suggestions and ideas for the authors of this variety of texts. Textbook writers should feel free to use SMSG texts in this way and to adapt, expand, and improve them for their own purposes. SMSG would appreciate being given proper credit in such cases, but at the same time it should be made clear that no endorsement by SMSG is implied.

There can be no doubt that the excellent materials produced by SMSG, UICSM, UMMaP, and other programs will have a profound effect on the production of improved materials of instruction for school mathematics.

EVALUATION OF TEXTS

When new commercial texts appear how shall we be able to determine whether or not they provide a satisfactory exposition of the new mathematics?

---

[1] SMSG *Newsletter* No. 6, March 1961, p. 9.

There is a principle of law that asserts that the best evidence of the contents of a document is the document itself. So it is with these new mathematics programs. The best way for a mathematics teacher to prepare himself to make valid judgments about new commercial texts is to become thoroughly familiar with at least one of the improved programs. This can best be accomplished by teaching one of the programs in its present form.

The superintendent should try to prepare his mathematics staff for the making of valid judgments in the selection of texts by:

► Giving some of his staff members an opportunity to teach the new materials now available.

► Supplying supervisory leadership that combines mathematical competence with a thorough knowledge of the new programs.

► Providing competent consultant services.

► Establishing an in-service training program to help teachers learn the characteristics and purposes of one or more of the improved programs.

SMSG Texts

How long will SMSG texts be available in their present form?

As long as they are needed. On January 28, 1961, the Advisory Committee of the School Mathematics Study Group adopted the following policy on the future availability of SMSG texts: [2]

Pending the availability of commercial texts along the general lines advocated by SMSG, each SMSG text will be kept available as long as it is needed. There will be an annual review, and when it is determined that a text is no longer needed, it will no longer be kept available. Suitable warning of such a decision will be given.

The SMSG texts are copyrighted and may not be reproduced without permission. Normally, permission will be granted for the reproduction of selections from SMSG texts for purposes consistent with those of SMSG.

The SMSG texts listed on page 54 are no longer to be regarded as experimental; they are now in their final revised form. All other SMSG texts are either in the initial stages or are undergoing revision on the basis of classroom experience.

Teacher Attitude

Some mathematics teachers are opposed to change. How can we overcome this opposition and get them interested in the new programs?

A first step toward overcoming such opposition is to understand the reasons for it. The teacher who has taught conventional mathematics for

---

[2] SMSG *Newsletter* No. 6, p. 9-10.

many years and has seen his pupils achieve a measure of success in their study of mathematics and science in college has every right to question both the need for and the superiority of the new programs. Moreover, many of these teachers realize that they are unprepared for the new programs, and this leads to a persistent sense of insecurity. The solution lies in helping them secure information about the new programs. The superintendent may say to his mathematics staff, "These new programs have been devised by mathematicians and teachers working together in a nationwide drive to improve school mathematics. This fact establishes a *prima facie* case in their favor which we cannot afford to ignore. Come, let us learn about the new programs so that we will have enough information to make valid decisions concerning them." Some teachers will accept this invitation immediately, and others will follow. It is our belief that teachers who become familiar with the new programs will find their opposition melting away along with the sense of insecurity which may have been the unconscious source of much of it. It is significant that teachers who have taught one of the improved programs are generally not willing to return to conventional materials and procedures.

If the majority of a mathematics staff is opposed to change, it would not be wise to force a new program upon them. It is reasonable, however, to insist that they learn about the new programs as soon as possible. This is their professional obligation, and their professional survival may depend upon it. In the meantime, encourage the willing minority to go ahead, and support their efforts in every way. Many teachers who are opposed to change reverse their positions when they see the results obtained by colleagues using the new material. The enthusiasm of students and teachers using the new materials is contagious.

Gaining Public Support

How can we convince the public that there is an urgent need for an improved program of instruction in secondary mathematics?

In his address Dr. Ferguson listed several procedures which were effective in his community. We offer several additional suggestions.

► It is better to emphasize the advantages of the new programs than to disparage the existing program. The keynote should be that because of the availability of improved materials of instruction, we are now in a position to establish a greatly improved program in school mathematics, and the demands of our times require that we initiate this program as soon as possible. The following advantages apply in varying degrees to any of the improved programs:

1. Explanations are given of the *why* as well as the *how*. The student learns that every bit of manipulation—"symbol pushing"—he does is valid for a reason.

2. Extensive use is made of deductive reasoning and proof. The basic laws of logic are applied to algebra as well as to geometry.
3. The structure of mathematics is emphasized. Mathematics is developed as an organized body of knowledge, founded on a surprisingly small number of basic assumptions.
4. The discovery method of teaching is utilized. Questions and illustrative examples often lead the student to make and test conjectures of his own. As a result, both the teaching and the learning of mathematics are more interesting and more rewarding than before.
5. Great emphasis is placed upon the precise use of language. Definitions are carefully stated. The ability to read intensively for meaning is essential for success.
6. The new courses are built on unifying ideas (function concept, real number systems, etc.) that are essential for the understanding of advanced mathematics.

► Parents should be told that the new program is not a course in mathematics made easy. Intensive study is still required, and parental aid should be enlisted in the matter of developing good study habits.

► The new program should not be referred to as "experimental." Instead there should be a description of the work done by the mathematics staff in preparing to teach the new program.

► There should not be a long time interval between the eliciting of public support and the actual initiation of the improved program.

► If any pupils cannot be included in the new program, the school officials should be prepared to explain why.

A statement for parents entitled *A Parent Looks at Modern Mathematics* may be obtained by writing to Frank B. Allen, Lyons Township High School, La Grange, Illinois.

A NATIONAL PROGRAM

We have heard several programs described. Is it expected that one program, perhaps a composite of those described, will emerge as the dominant program for the nation? If so, would it not be better to await the emergence of this program?

As Dr. Ferguson said, those who wait for the emergence of a national program will be left behind. The improvement of the mathematics curriculum, like the growth of mathematics itself, is a never-ending process. Perhaps some of the dominant elements common to all the improved programs will come to be widely accepted. We hope so. But as soon as this is accomplished, new improvements in structure, content, and presentation will be advocated. It is futile to wait for the emergence of a national program of instruction in school mathematics which will, like the *Pax Romana,* offer 200 years of stability. While you wait, many thousands of pupils will complete their years in secondary school without the benefits of improvements now available. Not one of the architects of the new programs wants adoption of a single program—even his own—in the nation's schools if this should mean the termination of all further efforts to improve school mathematics. Not one of them believes that his program is the ultimate answer. All of them would encourage other competent writers to develop their own expositions, and many of them intend to try to improve on their own product. Looking into the future, we cannot foresee stability—we can foresee only change. Teachers who begin to adjust to changes *now* will be in a much better position to keep pace with future changes.

Teaching Load

What modifications should be made in a teacher's load when he is assigned one of these new programs for the first time?

Extracurricular, clerical and other "cooperational" duties for those who are teaching one of these programs for the *first* time should be reduced or perhaps totally eliminated. Teachers will then have more time for preparation, and will also be available for after-school conferences with pupils who need help. Beyond this, we feel no general recommendation can be made. Much depends upon the teacher's competence and degree of preparation. Many able, well-prepared teachers have successfully taught one of the new programs for the first time without any reduction in the normal work load. They have, of course, put in many extra hours of work each day, but they felt compensated by the resulting improvement in their own professional competence. However, there are some teachers for whom a modification in work load would be appropriate during the first year of a new program. It has been suggested that a teacher who is teaching a new program at two different levels, each for the first time, should be assigned one class less than the standard load if he requests it.

Those who are selected to teach one of the new programs should know about it well in advance. The superintendent shares with them the responsibility for devising a study program designed to prepare them for the new assignment. It would be a mistake to assume that a reduction of teaching load during the first year can take the place of intensive preparation before the year begins.

Transfer Student

How can we provide for the student who transfers from a conventional program to one of the modern programs?

The transfer student has always been a problem. Each case should be considered individually. Some able students have demonstrated that they can make the transition from a conventional to an improved program in mid-year with some outside help, but such students are exceptional. One school has a student tutorial service, which seems to be remarkably effective in these cases. Most transfers from traditional classes, however, should be assigned to traditional classes. For this reason it may be desirable that schools changing to a new program maintain a few conventional mathematics classes during the transition period.

INDIVIDUAL DIFFERENCES IN ABILITY TO LEARN

BELOW-AVERAGE STUDENTS

What, if anything, do these programs offer to average and below-average students?

While the programs were, for the most part, written for college-capable students, some of them can be used effectively with pupils whose ability to learn mathematics is average or below average.

The University of Maryland material has been used successfully with all ability groups in grades 7 and 8. It has also been used for groups of slow pupils in grade 9. There are some schools where SMSG materials are used as the texts for all pupils in grades 7 and 8 regardless of their ability.

Special editions of the SMSG seventh and ninth grade texts have been prepared for slower students; the material was written at a lower reading level, and many additional concrete examples and simple problems were included. These special editions are now being tried in a variety of classes where the students proceed more slowly than those in the regular sections. The revision of these texts, on the basis of teacher reports, will continue through the summer of 1962. The final revisions, therefore, will not be available before September 1962.

SAME MATHEMATICS PROGRAM FOR ALL?

Should all students try to travel the same mathematical road as fast and as far as they are able? Should there be different sequences for the college-capable and the below-average groups? Should instruction for the latter group be closely geared to everyday problems and to social applications of mathematics?

One of the major defects of seventh and eighth grade mathematics curricula is that pupils of all ability levels are required to give too much attention to so-called practical applications. Most junior high school pupils are not fascinated by such topics as taxation, banking, interest notes, installment buying and other applications of the three cases of percent. Emphasizing such topics not only fails to motivate the learning of mathematics but actually serves to reduce substantially the amount of time that can be devoted to the development of new mathematical concepts. As a result, seventh and eighth grade mathematics has become largely a review of the arithmetic learned earlier with little or no advance in the pupils' understanding of mathematics.

Mathematics itself is interesting, and it can be presented in a form junior high school pupils are able to understand and appreciate if the pace and depth of presentation are adjusted to individual differences in ability to learn. This is the idea that motivated the writers of the UMMaP and SMSG materials for grades 7 and 8. They have produced a wealth of material which is interesting and fundamental to the development of important mathematical concepts. Consider some of the chapter headings for the SMSG course for grade 8: "Rational Numbers and Coordinates"; "Equations"; "Scientific Notation, Decimals, and the Metric System"; "Constructions, Congruent Triangles, and the Pythagorean Property"; "Real Numbers"; "Permutations and Selections"; "Probability"; "Similar Triangles and Variation"; "Non-Metric Geometry"; "Volumes and Surface Areas." A similar array of important and interesting concepts is provided in the seventh grade program, which is currently being revised for pupils who are less talented mathematically. Having produced sample texts for college-capable pupils, SMSG is now testing the hypothesis that all pupils can learn this interesting new mathematics if instruction is adjusted to individual differences in mathematical aptitude.

For some pupils the SMSG seventh and eighth grade program may require three years, and SMSG algebra (as revised for slower students) may prove to be an appropriate text for them in grade ten. There is mounting evidence that average and below-average pupils can, indeed, learn this new mathematics as well as or better than they learn the traditional mathematics.

This is encouraging. We believe that pupils of modest ability who proceed along the college preparatory sequence at their own pace gain much more than they would gain from one of the social-applications-review-of-arithmetic sequences now prevalent. However, the fact that slower pupils *can* learn the new mathematics does not mean that a slow-paced college preparatory program is necessarily the *best* program for them. We are here concerned with a very large group of pupils who deserve the consideration of having terminal courses in mathematics which are specially designed to meet their needs. The fact that adapted college preparatory courses have proved partially successful (and a decided improvement over conventional courses) does not relieve us of the obligation of trying to devise optimum programs for pupils who will complete their mathematics training in high school. We hope that this problem will receive the attention it deserves. A study of the learning process of slower pupils may suggest ways to improve texts for all pupils.

Homogeneous Grouping

Is it necessary for the successful presentation of these new programs that there be homogeneous grouping on the basis of ability to learn mathematics?

In our view, homogeneous grouping on the basis of ability to learn mathematics is an essential condition for the successful presentation of any mathematics program, traditional or modern. Ideally this grouping procedure should begin not later than grade 7. Many schools still face serious problems in carrying out grouping procedure in elementary grades and, therefore, start grouping after grade 7.

Readiness for Mathematics

We have all heard of ways to determine reading readiness. Is there any way to determine a pupil's degree of readiness for certain mathematical concepts?

In *The Process of Education* by Jerome S. Bruner (Harvard University Press), Chapter III is devoted to "Readiness for Learning." Arguments are put forth to support the hypothesis that mathematics can be taught effectively in some form to any child at any stage of his development. It seems clear from the experimental work of David Page, Robert Davis, Max Beberman, Patrick Suppes, and many others that we have grossly underestimated the mathematical power of students and their intellectual capacity to learn mathematics in all the grades from 4 through 12.

The successes that students have already had with UICSM, SMSG, and other experimental materials indicate that many students are ready for the simpler aspects of complicated mathematical concepts at a much earlier age than was thought possible a few years ago.

Advanced Placement

What bearing, if any, do these new programs have on the advanced placement program?

As Dr. Ferguson indicated, the advanced placement program in mathematics consists of a year of analytic geometry and calculus in grade 12. None of the improved programs provides such a course. They do, however, have a bearing on the advanced placement program in the sense that the four-year sequences provided (or planned) should be completed by prospective advanced placement students by the end of the eleventh year. It is the considered opinion of this panel that each of the programs described in this pamphlet provides an excellent introduction to the study of calculus.

THE MATHEMATICS CURRICULUM

OUTLINES OF THE PROGRAMS

While we all appreciate the limitations of an outline, would it not be worthwhile to provide outlines of the major programs as they now exist?

It would indeed. Following are the outlines for the programs of UMMaP, SMSG, Ball State, UICSM, and Boston College:

University of Maryland Mathematics Project

Mathematics for the Junior High School

First Book
1. Systems of Numeration
2. Symbols
3. Properties of Natural Numbers
4. Factoring and Primes
5. The Numbers One and Zero
6. Mathematical Systems
7. The Number System of Ordinary Arithmetic
8. Points, Lines, Curves, and Planes
9. Logic and Number Sentences
10. The System of Integers Under Addition
11. Plane Figures I
12. Scientific Notation for Arithmetic Numbers
13. Plane Figures II

Second Book
1. Chance
2. The System of Rational Numbers
3. Logic and Number Sentences
4. Equations
5. A System of Number Phrases
6. Factoring and Products in the System of Number Phrases
7. Fractional Number Phrases
8. The System of Real Numbers
9. Graphs on a Plane
10. Proofs and Equations in the System of Real Numbers
11. Plane Figures III
12. Measures, Estimates, and Approximates
13. Averages

School Mathematics Study Group

Mathematics for Junior High School

Volume I: Grade 7
1. What Is Mathematics?
2. Numeration
3. Whole Numbers
4. Non-Metric Geometry
5. Factoring and Primes
6. The Rational Number System
7. Measurement
8. Area, Volume, Weight, and Time
9. Ratios, Percents, and Decimals
10. Parallels, Parallelograms, Triangles, and Right Prisms
11. Circles
12. Mathematical Systems
13. Statistics and Graphs
14. Mathematics at Work in Science

Volume II: Grade 8
1. Rational Numbers and Coordinates
2. Equations
3. Scientific Notation, Decimals, and the Metric System
4. Constructions, Congruent Triangles, and the Pythagorean Property
5. Relative Error

6. Real Numbers
7. Permutations and Selections
8. Probability
9. Similar Triangles and Variation
10. Non-Metric Geometry
11. Volumes and Surface Areas
12. The Sphere
13. What Nobody Knows about Mathematics

First Course in Algebra   Grade 9
1. Sets and the Number Line
2. Numerals and Variables
3. Sentences and Properties of Operations
4. Open Sentences and English Sentences
5. The Real Numbers
6. Properties of Addition
7. Properties of Multiplication
8. Properties of Order
9. Subtraction and Division for Real Numbers

10. Factors and Exponents
11. Radicals
12. Polynomial and Rational Expressions
13. Truth Sets of Open Sentences
14. Graphs of Open Sentences in Two Variables
15. Systems of Equations and Inequalities
16. Quadratic Polynomials
17. Functions

Geometry   Grade 10
1. Common Sense and Organized Knowledge
2. Sets, Real Numbers, and Lines
3. Lines, Planes, and Separation
4. Angles and Triangles
5. Congruences
6. A Closer Look at Proof
7. Geometric Inequalities
8. Perpendicular Lines and Planes in Space

9. Parallel Lines in a Plane
10. Parallels in Space
11. Areas of Polygonal Regions
12. Similarity
13. Circles and Spheres
14. Characterization of Sets; Constructions
15. Areas of Circles and Sectors
16. Volumes of Solids
17. Plane Coordinate Geometry

Intermediate Mathematics   Grade 11
1. Number Systems
2. An Introduction to Coordinate Geometry in the Plane
3. The Function Concept and the Linear Function
4. Quadratic Functions and Equations
5. Complex Number Systems
6. Equations of the First and Second Degree in Two Variables
7. Systems of Equations in Two Variables

8. Systems of First Degree Equations in Three Variables
9. Logarithms and Exponents
10. Introduction to Trigonometry
11. The System of Vectors
12. Polar Form of Complex Numbers
13. Sequences and Series
14. Permutations, Combinations, and the Binomial Theorem
15. Algebraic Structures

Elementary Functions   Grade 12
1. Functions
2. Polynomial Functions
3. Tangents to Graphs of Polynomial Functions
4. Exponential and Logarithmic Functions
5. Circular Functions

Introduction to Matrix Algebra   Grade 12
1. Matrix Operations
2. The Algebra of 2 x 2 Matrices
3. Matrices and Linear Systems
4. Representation of Column Matrices as Geometric Vectors
5. Transformations of the Plane

Ball State Teachers College Experimental Program

Introduction to Mathematics
Unit One: Symbols and Numerals
1. Symbols
2. History of Numerals
3. Place Value and Bases
4. Base Ten

Unit Two: Rational Numbers
5. Definitions
6. Basic Principles of Addition and Multiplication
7. Factors and Prime Numbers
8. Number Pairs, Fractions, and Rational Numbers
9. Subtraction and Division
10. Inequalities and the Number Line
11. Applications

Unit Three: Real Numbers
12. Decimals
13. Irrational Numbers
14. Real Numbers
15. The Real Line

Unit Four: Algebra
16. Sets and Variables
17. Two Variables and Graphs
18. Negative Numbers
19. Inequalities, the Number Line, and Infinite Sets
20. "Story" Problems

Unit Five: Geometry
21. General Principles
22. Measurement
23. Plane and Space Figures
24. Perimeter, Area, and Volume
25. Similar Triangles and Trigonometry.

Algebra I
1. Sets and Counting
2. Symbols of Arithmetic and Algebra
3. Logic
4. Addition and Multiplication
5. Subtraction
6. The Integers
7. Some Applications of the Integers
8. Division
9. The Rational Numbers
10. Computing with Rational Numbers
11. Sentences, Relations, Graphs, and Functions
12. Polynomials
13. Equations Involving Several Variables
14. Extensions of the Rational Number System
15. Real Numbers
16. Quadratic Equations
17. Similar Triangles and Trigonometry

Geometry

1. Introduction
2. Logic
3. Concerning Lines
4. Congruence of Segments
5. Measurement of Segments
6. Congruence of Angles and Triangles
7. Use of the Congruence Theorems
8. Parallel Lines
9. Similarity of Triangles and Polygons
10. Area
11. Circles and Regular Polygons
12. Measurement of Angles and Arcs
13. Loci and Sets
14. Space Geometry
15. Analytic Geometry
16. Philosophy of Mathematics

University of Illinois Committee on School Mathematics

Unit	Descriptive Title
1	The Arithmetic of the Real Numbers
2	Generalizations and Algebraic Manipulation
3	Equations and Inequations
4	Ordered Pairs and Graphs
5	Relations and Functions
6	Geometry
7	Mathematical Induction

Unit	Descriptive Title
8	Sequences
9	Exponential and Logarithmic Functions (scheduled for publication in January 1962)
10	Circular Functions and Trigonometry (scheduled for publication in August 1962)
11	Polynomial Functions and Complex Numbers (scheduled for publication in August 1962)

Boston College Mathematics Series

Sets, Operations, and Patterns   Course 1

1. Development of Counting
2. Concept of a Set: Introductory Treatment
3. Operations. Addition, Multiplication, Division and Subtraction with Natural Numbers
4. Concept of a Relation
5. Concept of a Proof
6. Inverse Operations
7. Modulo Systems
8. Variable: Concept and Use
9. Equations. Linear Equations in One Variable. Solution Set
10. Treatment of Sets as a Mathematical Structure. Switching Circuits
11. Introduction to Measurement and Geometry
12. Tables: Primes, Factor Lattices

SOLID GEOMETRY

What has happened to solid geometry? Is it omitted from the new programs? If so, why should we downgrade space geometry in the space age?

The fact that none of the improved programs contains a course called *solid geometry* should not lead us to conclude that solid geometry is regarded as unimportant. There has been a change in the way space geometry is presented.

The consensus is that while the facts and principles of space geometry are important, solid geometry is not a good place to study deductive proof. The proofs are long and involved, and some of them cannot be properly explained without the use of calculus. For this reason a full semester of *deductive* solid geometry in grade 11 or 12 is no longer considered a justifiable expenditure of the pupil's time. Some of the important ideas of space geometry are approached earlier through plausible reasoning and appeals to the pupil's intuition. Indeed, a study of the outlines reveals that space geometry is not neglected in the overall picture. The SMSG sequence, for example, contains two strong units on space geometry in grade 8 and a unified treatment of plane and solid geometry in grade 10. In addition, three-dimensional rectangular coordinates and three-dimensional vectors are studied in grade 11.

A pupil who has completed this sequence certainly has more functional knowledge of space geometry than a pupil who has had the traditional course in deductive solid geometry, which contained no reference to vectors or to three-dimensional coordinate systems.

DEADWOOD

What traditional topics have been omitted in devising these new programs, and why?

Among the traditional topics omitted are the following: extensive computation with logarithms, extensive work on the solution of oblique triangles, some of the more elaborate cases of factoring, and a great many of the involved proofs of solid geometry. In his paper Dr. Price explained the reason for omitting the first two topics. In general, the content of any subject matter field must be based on an appeal to authority—the authority of leading scholars in that field. These topics are omitted because our leading mathematicians believe (*a*) they are no longer in the mainstream of mathematical thought, (*b*) they represent emphases that are no longer appropriate, and (*c*) the time devoted to their presentation is needed for the development of more important concepts. This idea was eloquently expressed in the Report of the Commission on Mathematics of the College Entrance Examination Board.[3]

The development of mathematics and the broadening of its applications have outrun the curriculum. Another way of putting this is to say that the present curriculum rests on a static rather than on a dynamic concept of mathematics. An analogy may help to dramatize the difference.

As a city grows, it becomes increasingly difficult to find adequate transportation from the center of the city to the outlying areas and the suburbs. The center is still the core of the city, but the streets are too narrow and too congested for the newer sections to be reached as quickly as the needs of the residents require. For a

---

[3] *Program for College Preparatory Mathematics.* New York: College Entrance Examination Board, 1959, p. 5-6.

time, systems of traffic lights and one-way streets suffice; but ultimately these patchwork methods, too, are found to be inadequate. Then there is constructed a limited-access freeway or expressway from the heart of the city to outlying points, bringing the newer regions effectively closer to the core.

Precisely this process is what the growth of mathematics demands—namely, that new and more efficient routes be found in the foundations of the subject as laid in secondary school to the newer territory of modern mathematics, in order that students may penetrate these newer territories without laboriously traversing all of the older content. In the process some obsolete or obsolescent material will be dropped, as will some material whose omission will cause regret. While still of value, it is of lesser value than the objective of attaining an understanding of the spirit, method, and content of contemporary mathematics.

GRADES 11 AND 12

What, if anything, can be done to give upperclassmen some of the benefits of the improved programs before they graduate? Specifically, would it be feasible to use the SMSG grade 11 text with juniors who have had traditional courses in algebra and geometry? Could the SMSG grade 12 text be used with pupils who have completed three years of conventional work?

If a qualified teacher is available, the answer is "yes" to the last two questions.

The first chapter of the SMSG eleventh grade book, *Intermediate Mathematics*, contains an extensive review and development of the basic ideas in the SMSG *First Course in Algebra*. After spending five or six weeks on this chapter, able pupils should be able to master the balance of the text, although this may require more than one year.

Good students who have had three years of traditional college preparatory mathematics will find both readable and fascinating the SMSG text for the one-semester course, Elementary Functions. Since this course provides an excellent introduction to the study of calculus, it is appropriate for the second semester of the senior year. The first semester might well be devoted to a study of those chapters in *Intermediate Mathematics* that the students have not covered in their previous work. Some able students may find it possible to study both Elementary Functions and the other SMSG one-semester course, Introduction to Matrix Algebra, in grade 12.

There are other materials that teachers of able upperclassmen should consider. For example, UICSM units 7 and 8, listed below, are now available; units 9, 10, and 11 will be published in 1962.

Unit	Topic
7	Mathematical Induction
8	Sequences
9	Exponential and Logarithmic Functions
10	Circular Functions and Trigonometry
11	Polynomial Functions and Complex Numbers

EVOLVING PROGRAM

Why can't we gradually absorb the new ideas and materials into the existing program without upsetting the applecart? Isn't it possible to achieve a great deal of improvement within the framework of the present program through the gradual introduction of new language, new topics, and new concepts?

This is possible. While it has the advantage that it gives the *teacher* time to become familiar with the new concepts and their possibilities in the classroom, the gradual introduction plan involves serious disadvantages and difficulties. Consider the first course in algebra. Suppose a teacher begins by introducing the commutative, associative, and distributive properties that Dr. Brown discussed. It is not sufficient merely to state these properties—*they must be used.* This leads to the idea of proof, which in turn requires the introduction of additional properties as well as attention to the question of what constitutes proof. Before long a competent teacher finds it necessary to introduce all the properties of an ordered field. The idea of order requires extensive work with inequalities, including their graphical interpretation. At this point the teacher finds that the traditional text does not state the necessary properties, nor does it provide the expositions and exercise materials necessary to exploit their far-reaching implications. Moreover, the discovery method of teaching, which is so essential in the approach to new concepts, is very difficult to use with traditional textbooks. This means that a great deal of time and energy must be expended in a frantic effort to supply mimeographed materials to supplement the text. In short, the teacher soon finds himself involved in rewriting the entire course. This is difficult (more difficult, in fact, than writing a new text), and most teachers do not have the time to do it properly. Why do it at all when some of our leading mathematicians stand ready to help by offering carefully written texts which accomplish the same purposes?

Our point is that improvements advocated by various writing groups are profound; they lead inevitably to intrinsic changes in both materials and methods. These changes cannot be accomplished by such superficial means as those used by a teacher who began an algebra course with a unit on sets, and having taken care of "the new mathematics," happily proceeded with the traditional text and made no further reference to the initial unit. This may be an extreme case, but this kind of superficiality is a hazard when the gradual introduction plan is used. If it is done poorly, it has little real effect. (In one school, after two years of "gradual improvement" the unit and final examinations remain unchanged.) Moreover, logical difficulties are always encountered when an attempt is made to use modern and traditional programs at the same time. Most teachers will do better to start with one of the new programs after taking the necessary training—and this procedure leads to improved results for pupils too.

SEQUENCE FOR GRADES 9 THROUGH 12.

Please describe a four-year mathematics sequence for (a) pupils who study algebra in grade 9 and (b) pupils who study geometry in grade 9 after having had a year of algebra in the eighth grade.

We shall give a tentative answer to this question, but it must be understood that each of the sequences we suggest is only one of several that might be used. The Commission on Mathematics said in its report: [4]

It should be noted that the character of the study of mathematics undergoes a change at about the twelfth-grade level; the sequential aspect of the study of mathematics begins to break down . . . the student's mathematical journey has brought him to a point from which he can proceed in many directions, all of them inviting.

This view serves to emphasize the need for competent counseling in school mathematics. Another factor that must be taken into consideration in suggesting a sequence is the ability level of the pupils involved. The fact that a pupil begins algebra in grade 8 usually does not insure that he is mathematically gifted and should follow the advanced placement program. For this reason, we suggest four distinct sequences. In the table on page 73, SMSG titles refer to courses based on those texts.

It is, of course, unfortunate if college-capable pupils have a gap in their mathematics training in grade 12. Such a gap would nullify the advantage of having studied algebra in grade 8. Therefore the entire six-year program (grades 7-12) should be planned before pupils begin the sequence. Such programs cannot be prescribed by outsiders; they must be planned by the mathematics staff under the direction of a competent supervisor.

ELEMENTARY CURRICULUM

Are there any related efforts to improve materials of instruction for grades K-6?

Yes. There are four major endeavors to improve mathematics in elementary school. The names and addresses of the directors are as follows:

Dr. E. G. Begle
School Mathematics Study Group
Stanford University
Stanford, California

Dr. Patrick Suppes
Stanford University
Stanford, California

Dr. Robert Davis
Madison Project
Syracuse University
Syracuse, New York

Dr. David Page
University of Illinois Arithmetic Project
College of Education
Urbana, Illinois

---

[4] *Ibid*, p. 30.

FOUR HIGH SCHOOL MATHEMATICS PROGRAMS

Grade	Regular Program	Regular Program (Algebra in Grade 8)	Advanced Placement Program	Advanced Placement Program—Algebra in Grade 8
9	Algebra	Plane and Solid Geometry	Algebra and some Intermediate Algebra	Plane and Solid Geometry
10	Plane and Solid Geometry	Intermediate Mathematics (Algebra ⅔, Trigonometry ⅓)	Plane and Solid Geometry	Intermediate Mathematics
11	Intermediate Mathematics (Algebra ⅔, Trigonometry ⅓)	Advanced Topics in Algebra, Elementary Functions *	Intermediate Mathematics (Very strong course)	Elementary Functions (semester), Analytic Geometry (semester)
12	Statistics and Probability (semester) Elementary Functions (semester)	Statistics and Probability (semester) Analytic Geometry (semester)	Analytic Geometry and Calculus	Calculus
	Begin Analytic Geometry and Calculus in College	Begin Calculus in College	Seek Advanced Placement in College	Seek Advanced Placement in College

* We suggest that this be a one-year course containing such units as Polynomial Functions, Circular Functions, Exponential and Logarithmic Functions, Theory of Equations, Mathematical Induction, Postulational Systems, Matrix Algebra.

COLLEGE CURRICULUM

What are the colleges doing to adjust their programs to meet the requirements of students who have had the improved mathematics in high school? Will such students be handicapped? What happens to a student with modern training in school mathematics who gets into a college with a traditional program?

Many of the better colleges and universities have already revised their mathematics courses and programs so that they and their students can take full advantage of the stronger preparation provided by the new high school mathematics programs, and students who have had the new programs will not be handicapped. Leadership in the revision of the college courses is being provided by the Committee on the Undergraduate Program in Mathematics of the Mathematical Association of America. College mathematics, according to this Committee, begins where the School Mathematics Study Group program leaves off. A student who has had a modern mathematics program for four years in high school will be bored if he is placed in a traditional freshman course in college algebra and trigonometry. Most colleges and universities offer advanced placement, so that a student can begin with the most advanced course for which he has the prerequisite knowledge.

COORDINATED CURRICULUM

Would it not be more logical to begin to improve the mathematics program in the elementary grades and work up from there? With all these programs being written simultaneously and by different groups, will it not soon become necessary to reorganize the entire sequence with a coherent pattern?

It would, indeed, seem more logical to establish a strong elementary program and then build the secondary program on this foundation. But there are good practical reasons for not proceeding in this manner. We must remember that the primary objective of this drive is to improve mathematics instruction for the college-capable student. The quickest way is to concentrate initially on the secondary program. A great deal can be accomplished here even before improved elementary programs are established. And in view of the needs of our times and of our students, it is urgent that present upperclassmen in our high schools have the advantages of these new programs.

Moreover, high school teachers are far more capable of adjusting to new programs than are elementary school teachers, who frequently have meager mathematics training and are generally expected to teach many different subjects in a self-contained classroom. If we recognize that the retraining of high school teachers is a difficult task, we must see that the retraining of a far larger number of elementary school teachers with little mathematics preparation is a far more difficult one. Therefore it is impractical to insist that an improved elementary program be prerequisite for an improved secondary program. The best strategy is to improve the secondary program as quickly as possible and then work down with the full realization that the secondary program can be further improved when a better elementary foundation has been provided. The entire sequence (K-12) will eventually require some coordination, and realignment is a small price to pay for the success we are now achieving.

TEACHER TRAINING—IN-SERVICE AND PRE-SERVICE

NEED

Can any of these programs be taught successfully by teachers who are accustomed to traditional programs and have not had special training?

No. All groups developing new programs have recognized that most teachers, through no fault of their own, are not properly equipped to present these programs successfully.

The extent of the supplementary education required depends upon the teacher's mathematical competence, teaching skill, and, in some measure, the program selected. Intensive preliminary study of the text and teachers' commentary is a prerequisite for successful use of either the UICSM or the SMSG program. Teachers who use the SMSG program will probably need consultant help during the first year. Many teachers who use the UICSM program will find supplementary training desirable to enable them to take full advantage of its greater emphasis on discovery and proof (see page 79).

PROVISION FOR IN-SERVICE TRAINING

How can we provide our teachers with the necessary in-service training?

School administrators have an important role in the provision of in-service training for mathematics teachers, both individually and through their professional organizations.

Individually, an administrator may

► Establish a study group within his own system in which teachers read and discuss the new programs and some of the materials designed to supplement them.

► Encourage teachers to take advantage of such opportunities for re-education as courses at nearby colleges and National Science Foundation summer and in-service institutes.

► Provide consultant help.

► Recommend that the Board of Education help meet the cost of summer training programs by providing books, tuition, and subsistence for teachers who do not gain admission to National Science Foundation summer institutes.

► Recommend that the Board of Education encourage teachers to attend professional meetings by paying expenses and providing substitutes.

By concerted action administrators can persuade the state university to cooperate with other colleges and universities in the establishment of training centers in key locations throughout the state to provide extension courses especially designed for teachers preparing for the new programs.

In some cases it may be more feasible to present such courses by television in the manner of Continental Classroom. Teachers may be given texts to accompany the television presentation, and the centers may provide consultant service and a place of meeting for discussion and examination sessions.

Type Required

What are the essential characteristics of an effective in-service training program?

We consider the following characteristics essential: [5]

► In-service courses should be taught in such a manner that they are not a threat to the status of any individual.

► The credit the teacher earns in these courses should apply toward meeting whatever requirements the school administration may have established with respect to continued education.

► The courses must serve to advance the teacher's understanding of mathematics with special emphasis on the ideas that undergird the new programs. This does not mean that such courses must be especially designed for a particular program, although this may be desirable in cases where the demand exists. Some in-service courses have made effective use of the school textbook (UICSM, SMSG, etc.) which the teachers are preparing to teach.

► The courses we envisage should present elementary mathematics from an advanced viewpoint. This means that mathematics courses designed for graduate students preparing for research are generally not suitable.

► Some of these courses should give attention to methods of presentation, but they should not be courses in methodology exclusively.

---

[5] For more detailed statements pertaining to the necessary re-education of teachers see Section 5 of the Report of the Commission on Mathematics, *Program for College Preparatory Mathematics* (College Entrance Examination Board, New York, 1959).

Materials Available

What materials of instruction (books, films, pamphlets, etc.) are available for in-service training programs?

In listing materials now available for in-service training, we should first call attention to the Teachers' Commentaries provided for the UICSM, UMMaP, and SMSG programs. In most cases the commentary is more voluminous than the text. While part of this bulk comes from the inclusion of detailed solutions to problems in the text, there is, in addition, a great deal of expository writing designed to give the teacher a deeper insight into the mathematics as well as an understanding of the reasons for certain methods of presentation. The text and commentary together provide an excellent basis for an in-service course.

The Panel on Teacher Training Materials of the SMSG has provided the following materials under the general heading "Studies in Mathematics":

Volume 1. *Some Basic Mathematical Concepts* (Set Theory), by R. D. Luce
Volume 2. *Euclidean Geometry Based on Ruler and Protractor Axioms*, by C. W. Curtis, P. H. Daus, and R. J. Walker
Volume 3. *Structure of Elementary Algebra*, by Vincent H. Haag
Volume 4. *Geometry*, by B. V. Kutuzov, translated from the Russian by the Chicago Survey of Recent East European Mathematical Literature
Volume 5. *Concepts of Informal Geometry*, by Richard D. Anderson.

Four additional volumes in this series will be published: three for elementary teachers and one on infinite decimals. The Panel has also prepared drafts of study guides in probability, number theory, and geometry and is currently working on drafts of study guides in logic and analysis.

The University of Illinois Committee on School Mathematics has produced 20 films which show how the UISCM material is taught by the discovery method.

A series of films based on the SMSG program has been produced by the Minnesota National Laboratories, State Department of Education, St. Paul 1, Minnesota.

Pre-Service Training

What college (pre-service) training should be provided for prospective teachers of mathematics? When can we expect the colleges to produce teachers who are prepared to teach these new programs when they graduate?

In answer to the first question, we support the report [6] by the Panel

---

[6] "Recommendations of the Mathematical Association of America for the Training of Teachers of Mathematics." *The Mathematics Teacher* 53:632-38, December 1960. Also available as a reprint.

on Teacher Training of the Committee on the Undergraduate Program in Mathematics, Mathematical Association of America. We hope this report will be given serious consideration by school administrators and other officials concerned with the strengthening of teacher certification requirements. It is time for all concerned to recognize that, other things being equal, the more mathematics a teacher knows the more effective he will be.

The answer to the second question depends partly on the discrimination shown by school administrators in employing recent graduates. In the last few years some colleges have done an excellent job of modernizing their teacher-training programs while others have done very little. With the Panel's report as a guide, an administrator or mathematics supervisor can quickly determine whether or not a candidate's qualifications are adequate for the level of instruction required of him. College authorities will be most responsive to any observations about the qualifications of their graduates. In short, administrators will get better qualified teachers when they demand them.

Further assistance is offered administrators in the form of a set of guidelines to be used by state departments of education in their evaluation of college departments of mathematics for the preparation of teachers of secondary school mathematics. These guidelines were prepared by the National Association of State Directors of Teacher Education and Certification, in cooperation with the American Association for the Advancement of Science. Copies may be obtained from the NASDTEC Project, 1515 Massachusetts Avenue, N.W., Washington 5, D. C.

METHODS OF INSTRUCTION

IMPORTANCE OF IMPROVED METHODS

Can most of the improvement we seek be obtained within the framework of the traditional programs and with conventional materials of instruction through the use of improved methods of teaching?

In general, no. Improved methods of teaching alone are not enough, nor is teachability the sole criterion for selecting content. Indeed there are many ideas that are eminently teachable, but probably should not be taught. The "invert and multiply" rule for dividing by a fraction is one example. Such rules serve only to improve manipulative skill at the expense of understanding.

We must realize that there have been profound changes in the content and structure of school mathematics as well as in methods of presentation. Indeed these new methods (discovery, emphasis on proof, etc.) do not stand alone but are to be regarded as essential concomitants of the new content. Conventional courses do not, in general, provide a basis for applying these improved methods. Hence, the use of conventional texts places severe limitations on the amount of improvement that can be achieved in methods of teaching. For these reasons, it is our opinion that any attempt to attain the objectives of these new programs by improved teaching procedures without giving attention to improved content and organization is bound to fail. We oppose such attempts on the same grounds that we oppose courses in methods of teaching mathematics that give little or no attention to the mathematics being taught.

Discovery

Is the discovery approach essential to all the new programs?

Yes. The discovery approach is utilized in varying degrees by all the new programs and is a central theme in the UICSM program. The effective use of this method requires teaching skill of the highest order. The teacher must be an expert interrogator, secure in his knowledge of mathematics, patient when pupils are slow to discover the obvious, capable of following some unexpected pupil suggestions, and considerate in rejecting others. He must know how to capitalize on the occasional explosions of understanding which characterize pupil reaction to this method, and he must avoid the too early verbalization of a principle that has been discovered. Those who don't know what we mean by *explosions of understanding* should see Professor Beberman's presentations in the UICSM films.

Emphasis on "Why"

Please give an example that illustrates how the improved programs stress the "whys" instead of the "hows."

It would be more accurate to say that the new programs emphasize *why* along with *how*. In his *Structure of Elementary Algebra* [7] Prof. Vincent Haag states the prevailing view: "A multitude of exercises is still absolutely necessary, but these techniques must be tied to the ideas from which they derive their validity."

As an example, consider the explanation of why $7 \times (-5) = -35$. At the outset there should be some cheerful examples about draining five gallons of water from a tank each hour for seven hours, spending five dollars a day for seven days, etc. In other words, the conclusion should be rationalized and rendered plausible. At some point, however, we should say to the student, "Look, on the basis of what we already know, the product here must be -35." The argument goes something like this:

---

[7] Vol. 3 of SMSG's Studies in Mathematics series.

$$7 \times 5 + 7(-5) = 7 [5 + (-5)]$$ Distributive property:
$$ab + ac = a(b + c)$$
$$= 7 \times 0$$ Property of additive inverse:
$$a + (-a) = 0$$
$$= 0$$ Multiplication property of zero:
$$a \times 0 = 0$$

Therefore $7(-5)$ must be another name for $-(7 \times 5)$ because $-(7 \times 5)$ or -35 is the only number which, added to (7×5), gives 0. Students should be required to give the reasons for each of the steps and they should generalize the argument to show that $a(-b) = -(ab)$. The teacher should explain the nature of these generalizations. Then the stage is set for proving that $(-a)(-b) = ab$. In this case we are thankful for the proof because plausible explanations are difficult to devise.

The *why* is emphasized when algebraic theorems are proved by using the properties of a field. In the traditional treatment these same theorems may be stated as rules showing how to get the answers.

The important consideration is that the pupil sees these rules as logical deductions from facts he has already accepted rather than as edicts handed down by the teacher.

PROGRAMED LEARNING

Do the new programs lend themselves to the use of teaching machines? Are any of them being programed?

Commercial publishers are showing considerable interest in mathematics, and some materials designed for programed instruction in mathematics have already appeared. The SMSG has appointed a Panel on Programed Learning, and plans are being made to present the ninth grade course (First Course in Algebra) in this format.

A word of caution would seem to be in order. We must not confuse improved programs of instruction (UICSM, SMSG, Ball State, UMMaP, etc.) with novel methods of presentation (teaching machines, programed texts). Some of the new programed courses may be excellent—but the fact that a course is programed tells us nothing about its quality. A course need not be good to be programed and a very good course could be programed poorly. If you are considering the use of programed instruction, we urge you to seek the advice of a qualified consultant.

TELEVISION

Has television been used to carry any of these new programs into the classroom? What are the realistic expectations for this means of improving instruction in mathematics?

For the past two years WHA-TV (Madison, Wis.) and WSN-TV (Milwaukee) have been televising a ninth-grade mathematics program. Some 100 classrooms and 3,000 pupils are involved. Television has also been used for teacher-training purposes, and we believe this is its greatest area of potential for improving instruction in mathematics. In considering the use of television we should remember that learning good mathematics requires a cooperative effort on the part of both student and teacher, and such cooperation is difficult with television.

TEAM TEACHING

Can the team-teaching method be used to capitalize on the master teacher's ability to present these new programs?

Yes, although we would rather not become involved in the team-teaching controversy. This is a problem about which school administrators are better informed than we are.

EVALUATION AND COMPARISON

HAWTHORNE EFFECT

To what extent are the successes of the new programs attributable to the enthusiasm engendered in both pupils and teachers by the fact that they are trying something new?

Two definitions come to mind. *Enthusiasm* has been cynically described as emotion without sufficient cause, and *fad* has been defined as a mistake that has been systematized. Experienced administrators have seen many fads come and go, and they have every right to probe the reasons for the success of these new programs. In replying, we must present evidence indicating that these new programs are not a fad—that they do, in fact, have lasting worth.

There is no doubt that the novelty of these programs does engender enthusiasm which in turn contributes to success. Yet experienced teachers know that such initial enthusiasm cannot sustain interest for very long— a few weeks at best. Our evidence shows that interest mounts as the year progresses. Moreover, teachers who have taught the improved materials have expressed an unwillingness to return to traditional programs. We believe that the enthusiasm of teachers for the improved programs is firmly founded in their conviction that these materials enable them to do a better job in the classroom. Our teacher panel has endorsed this view, and we earnestly believe that time will prove its truth.

BASIC SKILLS

Do the new programs provide enough practice exercises to build basic skills? Do pupils who have had these new programs show weakness in the basic skills and techniques of mathematics? Is there any supporting evidence for the statement that pupils in the experimental programs are able to "hold their own" on traditional standardized tests?

We believe that a study of the new materials will serve to allay any fears you may have about the lack of skill-building exercises. All the writing groups recognize the necessity of developing manipulative skills, and the desire to develop understanding as well contributes to the realization of this goal. The UICSM states that "acquiring manipulative skills and understanding basic concepts are complementary activities"; this is one of UICSM's major theses and is an accurate expression of the consensus of mathematics teachers.

As Dr. Ferguson stated in his paper, the evidence shows that the manipulative skill of pupils in the improved programs is at least as high as that of pupils in the traditional programs. This statement is supported by the following excerpt from a report made recently by E. G. Begle, Director of the School Mathematics Study Group:

> Studies carried out last year at the Minnesota National Laboratory indicated that students using the SMSG seventh grade text scored higher on routine mathematical skills at the end of the academic year than students in conventional courses, although a post test in the fall showed that this difference was no longer statistically significant. Similar but less conclusive tests in other grades gave strong indication that students did not suffer any loss in mathematical skills in classes using the SMSG texts. A more careful study of this is now being carried out by the Educational Testing Service.

The results of this more careful study should be available by fall 1961.

REVISION OF TESTS

To what extent are standardized tests being revised to measure the pupil's mastery of the concepts and techniques presented in the new programs?

The materials provided by the new programs are, in general, consistent with the 1959 recommendations of the Commission on Mathematics of the College Entrance Examination Board. The Educational Testing Service has stated that it will modify College Board examinations to bring them into line with the recommendations of the Commission. The publishers of commercial tests are not subject to the same influence, but there are indications that they too will modify their standardized tests.

APPLICATIONS OF MATHEMATICS

Effective learning often results from the study of practical problems. Are practical applications of mathematics given adequate attention in these new programs?

Every effort should be made to acquaint the pupil with a variety of applications of mathematics to other fields. The understanding of mathematics often grows out of an attempt to formulate and solve problems encountered in the sciences. Then, too, there are occasions when the pupil may be pleased to find an unexpected application of a mathematical principle that he learned in a completely abstract setting. Or he may observe that two seemingly diverse phenomena are, in fact, amenable to the same mathematical analysis. Such experiences serve to strengthen the pupil's understanding both of mathematics and of science. Therefore it is desirable to encourage coordination.

On the other hand, we are not inclined to criticize a mathematics text on the grounds that it does not contain a host of illustrations showing mathematics applied to other fields. Valid applications of school mathematics, suitable for inclusion in a text, are hard to find. They must not be too contrived, too trivial, or too remote from the pupil's experience to be meaningful. It is probably better to provide applications in the form of pamphlets to be studied as supplementary units by pupils who have the interest, experience, and scientific background to profit from such study.

The mathematics text must contain the principal ideas to be studied by all pupils, and it must be written in such a way that the teachers can build pupils' competence as expeditiously as possible. For college-capable pupils this is a practical procedure, because it will prepare them to study the calculus as college freshmen, enabling them to apply mathematics in their study of science at a level where this is very important.

PREPARATION FOR COLLEGE

What evidence supports the assertion that these new programs provide better preparation for college work in mathematics and science?

There is evidence that the graduates of UICSM, the oldest of the improved programs, have done exceptionally well in college mathematics and science. The other programs have not been operating long enough to have obtained such evidence. We believe that the most reassuring answer to this question comes from a consideration of how these materials were prepared. College mathematicians are the best authorities regarding the kind of school mathematics needed for the successful study of college mathematics, and they have helped to determine the content of the new programs.

6

Summary

• FRANK B. ALLEN

IMPROVEMENT in the instructional programs our schools provide for college-capable pupils depends on the kind of cooperation among university professors, school teachers, and school administrators that made these conferences possible.

The leading scholars in each field must take much of the responsibility for determining the nature of college-preparatory courses. Our mathematicians, until recently, have been too busy devising new mathematics to fulfill their obligations in this regard. Now some of them, like their counterparts in Europe, have produced expository materials that are useful in college-preparatory sequences. These materials, written with the aid and advice of classroom teachers, learning specialists, psychologists, and mathematics educators, delineate the patterns of reasoning that characterize mathematical thought. They spell out, in terms appropriate for each grade level, some of the implications of the explosive growth and manifold applications of twentieth century mathematics.

These new materials can be used to provide better preparation for the study of mathematics in college, thus relieving colleges of a heavy burden of remedial instruction and enabling students to learn more mathematics during their college years. For many students this means the attainment of the higher levels of mathematical literacy which are now necessary for the effective study of science, engineering, and many other subjects. For a few students it means earlier access to the frontiers of mathematical thought and longer careers as creative mathematicians. This is important because mathematicians are now in short supply, and mathematicians, like jet pilots, reach their maximum efficiency early in life.

Mr. Allen is chairman of the mathematics department at Lyons Township High School and Junior College, La Grange, Illinois.

The new programs in school mathematics will serve to increase the nation's supply of technicians, engineers, scientists, and mathematicians. They will also help, in some degree, to bridge the terrifying gap that now exists between mathematics instruction and the outrushing frontiers of mathematics and science. Indeed, they are typical of the programs that must be established in all fields (and are already being established in science) if the members of the next generation are to have the knowledge necessary to operate the complex civilization they inherit.

The teachers' role with respect to a new mathematics program is quite clear. We must be the guardians of that which is good in the traditional programs, the judges of clarity of exposition, the evaluators of new concepts from the standpoint of teachability, and, most important of all, the operators who transform theory into action in the classroom. We must not fail to criticize expositions that seem to be ineffective or materials that seem to be unteachable, for it is only through such constructive criticism that these expositions and materials will be improved.

At the same time, we must recognize the limitations of our role. It is not the function of teachers or of any organization of teachers to determine, unaided, what shall be taught in our schools. We must show the same appreciation for new mathematical ideas that we expect mathematicians to show for good teaching. We must, at all times, display the same positive attitude toward learning that we expect our pupils to display. We must remember that our decisions relative to teachability involve subjective judgments. Some concepts that seem at first to be unteachable are found on closer analysis to be appropriate for study by high school pupils. The teachability of a concept depends as much on the preparation and ability of pupils and teachers as on the inherent difficulty of the concept.

In the new programs we find that familiar ideas often have a strange appearance because of new symbolism. We need assurances that this new symbolism is not used merely to be modern, but rather to convey both old and new ideas as accurately and succinctly as possible. Our teacher panelists have given us such assurances with an eloquence that springs from conviction. Thus assured, we can proceed with the proper presentation of these new mathematical expressions. They are not substitutes for thinking. They are not a set of symbols whose manipulation miraculously produces valid conclusions. To present them thus would merely replace one kind of meaningless symbol-pushing with another. Instead we must present them as a new language which facilitates thought by enabling us to express abstract ideas with greater clarity.

There can be no question that a teacher gains well-deserved status in his school and in his community when he demonstrates an ability to teach the new mathematics. More important than this renewed recognition of the teacher as a scholar, however, is the teacher's deep satisfaction in the knowledge that he is doing a better job in the classroom.

The school administrator is the educational statesman who is called upon to supply the understanding and administrative guidance necessary for the success of the improved programs now available in several academic subjects. He is in a better position than the subject-matter specialist for a view of the entire picture.

In preparing for these conferences we sought the advice of a number of leading school administrators. Some school administrators see the drive to improve school mathematics as part of a nation-wide drive to achieve excellence in the classroom. Some view it as evidence that our schools have a new sense of mission which has its goals in high academic achievement. Many administrators are encouraged by the fact that the improved programs in mathematics, while designed primarily for the college-capable pupils, offer many ways to improve instruction for pupils who are mathematically less talented. They recognize the urgent need for improvement, but they do not regard the drive to improve school mathematics as a crash program whose sole justification is found in the menacing attitude of our potential enemies, and whose sole purpose is the production of mathematicians and scientists to serve, like nuclear weapons, as instruments of national survival. Instead, they regard it as a program for long-range improvement which aims to produce people who are not only more competent in science and technology but are also better able to meet the responsibilities of citizenship in a free society.

In recent months there have been many encouraging indications that mathematicians, teachers, and school administrators are gaining a better understanding of the role each group must play in a concerted effort to improve school mathematics. We hope *The Revolution in School Mathematics* will contribute to the effectiveness of this effort.

Appendix

SOURCES OF INFORMATION AND MATERIALS

Commission on Mathematics
College Entrance Examination Board
425 West 117th Street
New York 27, New York

For copy of report:
Commission on Mathematics
College Entrance Examination Board
% Educational Testing Service
Princeton, New Jersey

School Mathematics Study Group
Director: E. G. Begle
Stanford University
Stanford, California

For texts and teachers' commentaries:
Yale University Press
School Mathematics Study Group
92A Yale Station
New Haven, Connecticut

For other SMSG publications:
School Mathematics Study Group
Box 2029 Yale Station
New Haven, Connecticut

University of Illinois Committee on School
Mathematics
Director: Max Beberman
1208 West Springfield Street
Urbana, Illinois

Secondary School Curriculum Committee
National Council of Teachers of Mathematics
Chairman: Frank B. Allen
1201 Sixteenth Street, N. W.
Washington 6, D. C.

University of Maryland Mathematics Project
Director: John R. Mayor
College of Education
University of Maryland
College Park, Maryland

Ball State Teachers College Experimental
Mathematics Program
Director: Charles Brumfiel
Ball State Teachers College
Muncie, Indiana

Boston College Mathematics Institute
Director: Rev. Stanley Bezuszka, S.J.
Boston College
Chestnut Hill 67, Massachusetts

Developmental Project in Secondary Mathematics
Directors: Morton R. Kenner and Dwain
E. Small
Southern Illinois University
Carbondale, Illinois

Minnesota National Laboratory for the Improvement of Secondary School Mathematics
Director: P. C. Rosenbloom
Department of Education
301 State Office Building
St. Paul, Minnesota

Report on the Place of Science and Mathematics in the Comprehensive Secondary
School Program
National Association of Secondary
School Principals
(*Bulletin*, issue of September 1958)
1201 Sixteenth Street, N.W.
Washington 6, D. C.

Committee on the Undergraduate Program
in Mathematics
Mathematical Association of America
University of Buffalo
Buffalo 14, New York
or Prof. R. C. Buck
Mathematics Department
University of Wisconsin
Madison, Wisconsin

REGIONAL ORIENTATION CONFERENCES IN MATHEMATIC
October-December, 1960

Director: Frank B. Allen, Lyons Township High School, La Grange, Illinoi

Sponsored by: National Council of Teachers of Mathematics
Phillip S. Jones, President
M. H. Ahrendt, Executive Secretary

With the financial support of: National Science Foundation

THE CONFERENCES

Time and Place	*Director*	*Region*
October 3–4 Philadelphia	M. Albert Linton, Jr. William Penn Charter School Philadelphia, Pennsylvania	Connecticut, Delaware, District of Columbia, Maine, Maryland, Massachusetts, New Hampshire, New Jersey, New York, Pennsylvania, Rhode Island, Vermont
October 10–11 Iowa City	H. Vernon Price University of Iowa Iowa City, Iowa	Illinois, Iowa, Minnesota, Nebraska, North Dakota, South Dakota, Wisconsin
October 27–28 Atlanta	H. Mark Huie Board of Education Atlanta, Georgia	Alabama, Georgia, Louisiana, Mississippi, North Carolina, South Carolina, Virginia
November 3–4 Portland	William W. Matson Public Schools Portland, Oregon	Alaska, Idaho, Montana, Oregon, Washington, Wyoming
November 18–19 Los Angeles	Clifford Bell University of California Los Angeles 24, California	Arizona, California, Hawaii, Nevada, Utah
December 1–2 Topeka	Marjorie L. French Topeka Central High School Topeka, Kansas	Arkansas, Colorado, Kansas, Missouri, New Mexico, Oklahoma, Texas
December 9–10 Miami	Agnes Y. Rickey 1410 N. E. 2nd Avenue Miami 32, Florida	Florida, Puerto Rico
December 15–16 Cincinnati	Mildred Keiffer Board of Education Cincinnati 6, Ohio	Indiana, Kentucky, Michigan, Ohio, Tennessee, West Virginia

STEERING COMMITTEE

Max Beberman Urbana, Illinois	Edwin C. Douglas Watertown, Connecticut	G. Baley Price Washington, D. C.
E. G. Begle New Haven, Connecticut	Phillip S. Jones Ann Arbor, Michigan	Mina Rees New York, New York
Kenneth E. Brown Washington, D. C.	John R. Mayor Washington, D. C.	H. Van Engen Madison, Wisconsin
	Philip Peak Bloomington, Indiana	

CONSULTANTS TO THE STEERING COMMITTEE

Harold P. Fawcett Columbus, Ohio	Mary Hovet Ellicott City, Maryland	Bruce E. Meserve Montclair, New Jersey

CONFERENCE CONSULTANTS

Frank B. Allen La Grange, Illinois	Kenneth E. Brown Washington, D. C.	W. Eugene Ferguson Newtonville, Massachusetts
	G. Baley Price Washington, D. C.	

PANELISTS

Banks, Wilson, Pleasant Valley-Riverdale High School, Bettendorf, Iowa

Brown, Ruth, McKinstry Junior High School, Waterloo, Iowa

Carstairs, Ellen A., Eckstein Junior High School, 3003 East 75th Street, Seattle 15, Washington

Cobb, Lela, 3820 East Orme, Wichita 18, Kansas

Egbers, Eldon B., Public Schools, Seattle, Washington

Epperson, Eugene R., 1013 South Locust Avenue, Oxford, Ohio

Epstein, Jess, Educational Testing Service, 20 Nassau Street, Princeton, New Jersey

Friend, Carol, North Miami Beach Junior High School, 20821 N. E. 13th Place, North Miami Beach, Florida

Garstens, Helen L., Associate Director, University of Maryland Mathematics Project, University of Maryland, College Park, Maryland

Glenn, William H., Vice-President, National Council of Teachers of Mathematics, 351 South Hudson Avenue, Pasadena, California

Hanna, Paul, Richmond Senior High School, Richmond, Indiana

Hildebrandt, Martha, Mathematics Department, Emory University, Atlanta 22, Georgia

Hill, Thomas, 1909 North Douglas Street, Oklahoma City, Oklahoma

Hughes, S. M., Chairman, Mathematics Department, Melbourne High School, 424 Lagoon Avenue, Melbourne, Florida

Jameson, Richard E., Yorktown Senior High School, Arlington, Virginia

Kalman, Karl S., Head, Department of Mathematics, Abraham Lincoln High School, Philadelphia, Pennsylvania

Kansky, Robert, Melbourne High School, Box 371, Melbourne Beach, Florida

Large, Emma Mae, Dean, Mary Holmes Junior College, West Point, Mississippi

Levine, Maita, 3975 Warwick Avenue, Cincinnati 29, Ohio

Linkhart, Bonnie, Catalina High School, 3645 East Pima, Tucson, Arizona

Lunger, John P., 102 John Tyler Highway, Williamsburg, Virginia

Lynch, Martha, 1268 Piedmont Avenue, N. W., Atlanta 9, Georgia

Marston, Howard, Route 1, Box 242, Ellisville, Missouri

Moore, Frances, Athens High School, Athens, Georgia

Moredock, Stewart, Sacramento State College, Sacramento, California

Nelson, Sara L., Head, Mathematics Department, Georgia State College for Women, Milledgeville, Georgia

Peckenham, Jesse K., 6078 Colton Boulevard, Oakland 11, California

Rathert, Pauline, 815 East 58th Street, Indianapolis, Indiana

Schaaf, Oscar F., Head, Department of Mathematics, South Eugene High School, 123 Leigh Street, Eugene, Oregon

Sister Mary of the Angels, Director, Mathematics Department, St. Rosalia High School, 411 Greenfield Avenue, Pittsburgh 7, Pennsylvania

Small, Dana, Franklin High School, 3650 S. E. Knight, Portland 2, Oregon

Tanzer, Joan, Mechanical Arts High School, St. Paul, Minnesota

Wandke, Grace, Barrington Consolidated High School, Barrington, Illinois

Warren, Leonard, Paul Revere Junior High School, 16115 Sunset Boulevard, Pacific Palisades, California

White, Edward, 458 Garver S. W., Camden, Arkansas